W9-DHF-849

PROPERTY OF
PHYSICS DEPT.

Toward a Scientific Theology

Toward a Scientific Theology

Ralph Wendell Burhoe

CHRISTIAN JOURNALS LIMITED
BELFAST :: DUBLIN :: OTTAWA

First Edition 1981 by Christian Journals Limited, BELFAST
BT9 6TH and 760 Somerset Street W, Ottawa, Ont. Canada.

Copyright © Christian Journals Limited 1981

All rights reserved. This book is sold subject to the conditions
that it shall not, by way of trade or otherwise, be lent, re-sold,
hired out or otherwise circulated without the publishers' prior
consent to any form of binding or cover other than that in
which it is published and without a similar condition including
this condition being imposed on the subsequent purchase. No
part of this publication may be reproduced, stored in a retrieval
system, or transmitted, in any form or by any means, elec-
tronic, mechanical, photocopying, recording or otherwise,
without the prior permission of the publishers. Chapters 2-7
were originally published in *Zygon: Journal of Religion and
Science*. © 1971, 1967, 1972, 1973, 1976, 1980 by the Joint
Publication Board of the Institute on Religion in an Age of
Science and the Center for Advanced Study in Religion and
Science at the University of Chicago Press, and reprinted with
permission.

Burhoe, Ralph Wendell
   Toward a Scientific Theology
 I. Burhoe, Ralph Wendell
II. Religion and Science – 1946 – 215   BL241.517

ISBN 0 904302 70 9

Cover designed by Sandy Ferguson

Made in Ireland

Contents

To Calla and Frances, my close helpmates in
this work through fifty years, and to the
hundreds of scientists and scholars without
whose encouragement, cooperation and
wisdom the book would not be.

Foreword

By Don Browning

The following essays were written by Ralph Burhoe over a period of fifteen years from 1965 to 1980. Professor Burhoe was the winner in 1980 of the prestigious Templeton Prize for Progress in Religion. He is also widely known as the founding editor of *Zygon: Journal of Religion and Science* as well as the founder of the Institute on Religion in an Age of Science (IRAS) and the Center for the Advanced Study of Religion and Science. From 1964 to 1974 he was Research Professor of Theology and Science at Meadville/Lombard Theological School affiliated with the University of Chicago.

He received the Templeton Prize for both his theoretical contributions to the science-religion dialogue and his outstanding work in stimulating an extensive conversation of growing importance between leading scientists and theologians. At a time when conversation between religion and science was almost nonexistent, Ralph Burhoe, in his writings, his organizational and promotional skills, and his great personal contact and rapport with both scientists and theologians, has been at the center of a growing conversation, international in scope and of momentous importance.

Over the last twenty years, Ralph Burhoe has authored more than a hundred articles on various topics pertaining to the dialogue between science and religion. The essays included in this volume are representative of the direction of his work as this has developed over the last decade. They are papers which were written in some cases for specific conferences where

professional scientists, theologians, and interested lay people
met to discuss the relation of science and religion. Some of
them were given at the conferences of the Institute on Religion
in an Age of Science. All but the first of these papers have been
published in *Zygon*.

The first chapter is Professor Burhoe's acceptance speech
delivered at the public ceremonies, held at Guildhall London,
celebrating his winning of the Templeton Prize. The opening
pages of this lecture constitute a simple biographical statement
recounting the motivations and events which led him to make
the dialogue between science and religion the consuming concern of his life. The conclusion of the statement is a rather
compact outline of the direction that his thought has taken
during the last few years. The essays that follow are organized
chronologically and record a series of investigations and probes
in Professor Burhoe's efforts to develop an increasingly more
refined position on the relation of science and religion. These
articles have not been edited for the purpose of this volume,
except for a few typographical errors and a few words for
clarity; they are presented in their original published form and
constitute a map of Ralph Burhoe's pilgrimage.

The title of this volume, *Toward a Scientific Theology,* points
to what is unique about it. Professor Burhoe is not attempting,
in the fashion of a Karl Barth or an Anders Nygren, a science
of theology. He is not attempting a systematic and coherent
presentation of the meanings of the Christian faith for the
purposes of a confessing church. Burhoe's work presupposes,
and admittedly does not always recognize the intricacies of, the
exegetical and hermeneutical tasks which have been the preoc-
cupation of most of recent European and American theology.
Ralph Burhoe is attempting an additional step; he is seeking to
find ways to reconcile the central themes of the Judeo-
Christian tradition with the dominant paradigms operative in
the human sciences—especially evolutionary biology, genetics,
physics, and certain strands of modern psychology. He is
working to develop a theology that can be stated in the
theoretical terms used to explain biological and cultural evolution. He takes a functional approach to religion; he assumes
the phenomenologically-given meanings of religion and then
goes further and attempts to determine the functional role that

particular religious expressions play in people's struggles creatively to adapt to the selective powers of their environment.

His major thesis here is that religions have played a crucial role in producing higher levels of altruistic behavior in humans as they have evolved from apes to persons capable of cooperation in complex, interdependent, advanced, urban societies. Religion stimulates cultural adaptation and evolution; it constitutes the controlling values at the top of the hierarchy of cultural values guiding human adaptation and progress. Religion has the twofold task of preserving the successful adaptive maneuvers that humans have hit upon, as well as of renewing humans when despair has nearly extinguished all hope. Furthermore, if religion dies, mankind will lose this powerful civilizing agent, perhaps never to be replaced.

There are other individuals, mainly social scientists, who share some of the features of Professor Burhoe's view of religion. It has continuity with perspectives going back to the philosophies of William James and John Dewey. What is unique, however, is Burhoe's vigorous attempt to go beyond the neutral attitudes of the descriptive scientist and apply this view directly to the task of constructing a normative theological position. This he does with the benefit of recent advances in theoretical biology and genetics. Some people will believe that Professor Burhoe goes too far in this direction; others will object to the details of his position. But there are others who believe his work constitutes an important and suggestive dimension of a future agenda for theology, one sadly neglected in the recent past.

Don Browning

Alexander Campbell Professor
of Religion and Psychological
Studies, Divinity School,
The University of Chicago

1

*Introduction**

RELIGION around the world in this twentieth century has manifested itself as tragically less than adequate for human welfare or salvation in an age of the dangerously explosive expansion of scientific *knowledge* and scientific *technology*. Beginning in the West, where modern science developed, there has been during recent centuries a widespread loss of religious belief—and with it a loss of meaning and moral motivation—because of religion's seeming incompatibility with a more credible new truth. Similar impacts from Western science have begun to hit Islam, Hinduism, and other religions of the world.

Yet a careful examination of the human predicament, initiated by a group of scientists about forty years ago and participated in by hundreds of scientists and scholars of religion ever since, gives a more hopeful picture of religion. From this group now come published conclusions that religion has been essential in transforming ape-men into civilized humans capable of gladly cooperating in large societies. This group further says that man will forever need religion and that the revitalization of religion is required if high civilization is to survive.

It should be noted that these recognitions of the importance of religion originated not from professional defenders of the church but rather from often agnostic scientists on the basis of

---

*Edited version of the address given by Ralph Wendell Burhoe
On Accepting the Templeton Prize for Progress in Religion
(The Guildhall, London, 13 May 1980)

13

pictures given by modern evolutionary theory about human nature and destiny.

How did I become involved in such a group that looked at religion scientifically?

I grew up in a family where religion was taken seriously. They read about it, went to meetings about it, and taught others about it. Among family and friends I was much impressed with the difference that serious belief in sound religion seemed to make in quality of life—in terms of morals, helpfulness to others, courage, hope, and meaningful activities. A child living close to them could observe them, even when their hair was down. I was so impressed with an observable correlation between what people really believed and the quality of their lives that I could not believe the conclusions of many social-science studies since the 1930s that there is no good correlation between virtuous behavior and religion. My own observations convinced me that these studies merely said that you cannot expect high fig production from trees that only look like fig trees.

In my childhood I had readily believed my parents' religious tradition, but already in high-school science I began to experience how religious belief tended to be eroded whenever the religious teachings became doubtful in the context of seemingly more reliable truth. Since my Baptist tradition purported to persuade on the basis of reasonable evidence of truth, I was early involved in various attempts to resolve the puzzle of what is truth. In Harvard College I became convinced the sciences were man's most advanced tools for discovering what was true and I studied in them widely. After that I went to Andover Newton Theological School to explore my prime concern: to find a way to interpret religion credibly in the light of the sciences. But financial circumstances and the coming of my own children required me to leave school, go to work for twelve years at Harvard's meteorological observatory, and to puzzle on religion and science in my spare time.

An Invisible College for Scientific Study of Values and Religion

In 1947 I found one of the most ideal positions possible for my concerns, a new position of Executive Officer, just opened up by the American Academy of Arts and Sciences—a sort of American Royal Society with headquarters in Boston. Its officers and Council wanted me to assist committees of the Fellows of the Academy to accomplish various goals under an extension of its 1780 charter, "to cultivate every art and science which may tend to advance the interest... of a... people." A prime goal was to update our "philosophical, moral, and political foundations" to adapt them to the conditions of a new century and of a whole world of people made interdependent by scientific technology. I was given a wonderful opportunity to work with some of the best minds in many disciplines, in programs to make sense of various human problems.

To my delight, I found among Academy Fellows a number of scientists and other scholars in diverse disciplines who were interested in understanding the nature of human values. In 1940 physiologist Hudson Hoagland and astronomer Harlow Shapley had organized a committee on science and values. In 1950 some of these and others stated: "we believe that the sudden changing of man's physical and mental climate brought about by science and technology in the past hundred years has rendered inadequate some ancient institutional structures and educational forms, and that the survival of human society depends on the re-formation of man's world view and ethics, by grounding them in the revelations of modern science as well as on tradition and intuition." The committee was reorganized to explore this problem and to encourage and cooperate with other groups to the same end. At a meeting on 8 May 1952 under the chairmanship of biochemist George Wald, committee members agreed, that "because of the importance of religion to our social structure," we should share some of the newer and better interpretations of the implications of the sciences for religion with clergy who expressed interest.

Stemming from the direction developed at that meeting, I sought a suitable forum. I had become a Unitarian, and my minister, Dana McLean Greeley, put me in touch with Methodist theologian Edwin Prince Booth, and Unitarian clergyman Lyman V. Rutledge, who had led the establishment of an annual, interfaith, week-long conference on The Coming Great Church. They welcomed our ideas and with them we organized

in 1954 the Institute on Religion in an Age of Science. The
work of the Institute led, ten years later in 1964, to my
accepting the invitation of President Malcolm R. Sutherland
and the Trustees of Meadville/Lombard Theological School
affiliated with the University of Chicago, to head what may
have been the first theological-school-sponsored department
ever commissioned to research, develop, and teach theology
using the modern sciences as a prime resource.

At Meadville in 1965 we established the Center for
Advanced Study in Theology and the Sciences, which later
became the independent Center for Advanced Study in Religion and Science, now affiliated with the Chicago Cluster of
Theological Schools and led by Professor Philip Hefner. In
1966 Meadville's Center for Advanced Study, in cooperation
with the Institute on Religion in an Age of Science and the
University of Chicago Press, first published the new scholarly
periodical—*Zygon: Journal of Religion and Science*—to communicate to a larger audience our studies as well as studies by
others whom we found to be working in similar ways to relate
religion and science. *Zygon* has helped create a community of
pioneers around the world. It now continues its generative role
under a new, younger chief editor-publisher, Professor Karl
Peters of Rollins College in Florida.

I cannot here name all the groups with which I have worked.
But the international roster of the many hundreds of persons
(through the Academy committee, the Institute, the Center,
Zygon, etc.), who for more than thirty years have interacted to
generate and test in the light of the sciences a new understanding and appreciation for long-standing sources of human values, including religion, have constituted an invisible college
which has greatly advanced this field. I believe it may provide
grounds for a reformation and revitalization of religion, more
broadly credible in an age of science.

Religion Seen Scientifically

In accepting the Templeton Prize for Progress in Religion, I
should tell you at least a little about my own contributions to
understanding religion in the light of the sciences. In addition
to organizing and publishing symposia, I have engaged in my

own extensive research to apply the sciences so as to add to our understanding of religion in ways akin to our understanding of the heavens, the earth, and the creation of life and man. I have believed that this could be as helpful to religion as scientific theory generally has been to human needs in agriculture, medicine, and other areas of applied science. Here I shall tell you of some findings exciting to me. I have published more on them in my "Religion's Role in Human Evolution" and other papers.

I have found modern evolutionary theory the best route to understanding religion and I have found religion a necessary element in making sense of human evolution. In particular, my hypothesis about the role of religion provides, I believe, the best scientific explanation for what sociobiologist E. O. Wilson has called the "culminating mystery of all biology." By this we mean the mystery of how humans can be altruistic and live cooperatively in large societies when natural selection has barred other creatures from conspecific behavior of this sort except to benefit very close kin. This barrier was clearly shown more than 15 years ago by such developers of evolutionary theory as W. D. Hamilton (in Britain) and George C. Williams (in the United States). In 1976 it was fascinatingly described by Oxford's Richard Dawkins in his *The Selfish Gene*.

The weight of evidence forces me to concur (with Hamilton, Williams, Dawkins, and the bulk of evolutionary theorists) that genetic evolution can produce altruism only to benefit close kin. How then do humans become motivated to be helpful, even risking their bodies for nonkin? I believe that Dawkins was moving in the right direction for a solution to this when he developed a theory of the evolution of cultural information analogous to the evolution of genetic information, akin to one some of us had begun to develop before 1962 (see *Evolution and Man's Progress* edited by Hudson Hoagland and me). But Dawkins was a keen enough scientist to recognize immediately that even though a kind of natural selection of "memes" (his name for cultural evolution's analogue of genes) may be the correct model, it cannot explain human altruism, for the same reason that natural selection of genes cannot—selection is that which favors the selected, not others. To continue in being, competing memes must be as selfish as competing genes.

Donald T. Campbell's presidential address to the American Psychological Association in 1975 and earlier papers had presented a related theory of a natural-selection process operating in cultural evolution and, much more than other sociobiologists, he included religion as a necessary factor to produce altruism. My own natural history of religion started with my "A Scientific Theory of the Soul" (presented on 21 April 1950 to the Society for the Scientific Study of Religion). In 1969, Campbell's insistence on Williams' thesis, prodded me to tackle the mystery of how biosocial evolution could produce altruism. My papers credit religion (even more than Campbell, Dawkins, or Wilson) as the primary agency and I show religion itself to be a product of natural selection that has coadapted culturetypes with genetic DNA.

In particular, I think I have shown how human evolution overcame natural selection's barrier to cooperation among competing genes or memes. This solution came to me in pondering the work of the late Alfred E. Emerson of the University of Chicago, who was a specialist on termites and their societies. He observed complex societies of insects and other species interacting as mutually supportive elements in a small, local unit of the ecosystem that functioned almost as an organism. This could be explained, he thought, only if the ecosystem unit were selected as a unit of life, which he called a "supraorganism." Since the adaptation of any number of separate species to perform mutually supportive functions with other species in a common ecosystem involves adaptation to circumstances outside the species, it completely avoids the Hamilton-Williams genetic barrier to the evolution of nonkin cooperation within a species. This possibility was suggested by Williams in his classic 1966 *Adaptation and Natural Selection,* who added that, in these symbiotic mutualisms, "the selection of alternative alleles can simply and adequately explain the origin and maintenance of such relationships."

While this gives a genetic base for the evolution of Emerson's supraorganisms of mutually cooperative actions among different species, it will not account for the evolution of human societies, where each person is of the same species, unless we should find that the culturetypes of human societies somehow are the "genes" of a new "species" of life, a species with which the genes of ape-men have become coadapted to form a new kind of ecosystemic supraorganism because the mutual benefits for viability to the participating species exceed the benefits given by previous or competing systems.

I submit that a close look at the facts of human evolution already reveals that this is just what has happened. The "culturetype," (the information packet, including language, religion, etc.), that shapes the behavior of a sociocultural organism, is indeed selected independently from, but coadapted with, the more ancient packets of genetic information, the genotypes that guide the basic development of ape-man organisms. From widespread evidence, it is overwhelmingly clear that it is the sociocultural context of our upbringing and not our genes that gives us our "native" language, our religion, etc. Reciprocally, it is equally clear that most persons from any genetic population readily absorb the characteristic language, religion, etc. of the culturetype in which they are reared. Insofar as a culturetype produces a living sociocultural system or organism, then each individual reared in it may be said to be an *internal* or *endo*-symbiont. That the culturetype does produce an independent, living organism which is of such a character that it can interact with a population of hominid endosymbionts to produce supraorganisms that we call human societies is a matter whose justification I can sketch here only too briefly.

Lewis Thomas in his *Lives of a Cell,* in a chapter on "Organelles as Organisms," describes an analogous, much older system of symbiotic, well-coadapted species. In it he tells of molecular biology's recent picture of the body of each animal or human as not a single species but as a sort of Emersonian supraorganism or ecosystem consisting of populations of two or more cooperating species whose gene pools evolve independently. Each of the billions of cells of our bodies now appears to be such a symbiotic ecosystem. Molecular biology seems to be revealing that while some general features of the behavior and structure of our cells are directed by our hominid genotypes, much of what goes on inside of each cell is carried on by the subcellular populations of more primitive, alien organisms with their own genetic DNA that has evolved independently from the cell's genotype. Of course, our theory and the facts suggest that the central genotype and the genes of

the several endosymbiotic species have been mutually
coadapted to provide reciprocal benefits so that each species
prospers and the collectivity of their behaviors results in a
viable Emersonian supraorganism—an organized, local,
ecosystemic unit.

Protoreligion in my model arose over a million years ago as
the agency which remembers and culturally transmits the basic
long-range values or goals of the sociocultural organism, goals
necessarily so closely coadapted with the genetically programmed goals in a hominid population as to elicit strong symbiotic
mutualism. Religions, by enculturating certain common patterns in the outer layers of the genetically organized brains of
such populations, provided a habitat that persistently transformed the expression of the goals of those genes so that an
adaptation was produced that was better than any competing
structuration, simultaneously for the individual and for the
cultural organism to which he was bound. In recent millennia,
aided by the emergence of writing and other relevant cultural
developments, religions have rapidly expanded the potential
population size of viable cultural organisms and provided a
habitat into which the bulk of the ape-man populations found it
adaptive to move, as they were freed from limitation to small
kinship groupings.

We need to understand this sociocultural "habitat" as
analogous to the habitats that Thomas's cells or Emerson's
termites provided for their endosymbionts at earlier stages of
evolution. Such a habitat is a living envelope that contains
information or boundary conditions that both protect the
endosymbionts and guide them into a larger life. Significant for
the worth of each individual is that, reciprocally, his brain
provides a habitat for a significant fraction of the characteristic
information or culturetype that shapes the cultural organism,
particularly its basic mores, values, or religion. The brain is the
integrating seat of the two major symbionts of human nature:
the individual animal and the sociocultural system. Moreover,
since the culturetype and the genotype are bodies of information adapted to requirements for life in the same ecological
niche, then an ape-man's brain could produce awareness of and
desire to serve not only its body, but increasingly also its

society and the ecosystem that sustains both, when these sacralities were suitably symbolized by religion.

In the evolution of this endosymbiosis of ape-man populations in a sociocultural organism, natural selection tends to remove disadvantageous elements of the gene pool and (provided there exists competition among culturetypic elements—a basic reminder of the value of social freedom) also to remove the disadvantageous elements from the religious and other sectors of the culturetypes. The scientific pictures join the religious myths in saying that the same system of reality and power that created the earth and life upon it also created, sustains, and judges human life, including our religions. It makes little difference whether we name it natural selection or God, so long as we recognize it as that to which we must bow our heads or adapt.

Thus religion became a central, forever necessary element of human nature by its role in the coadaptation that formed a mutually beneficial symbiosis between the hominids and the new transgenetic kingdom of life that emerged in hominid brains as shaped by cultural information. It should be noted that in a dynamically evolving system there are constant steps of change or reformation, from which religions are not exempted. If two mutually sustaining symbionts undergo changes such that one is debilitated, the total system (including all symbionts) may also be debilitated. If the exchange of benefits becomes unbalanced, one of the two species becomes a parasite upon the other. The sociocultural organism, including its religious agency, sometimes becomes ill-adapted and a parasitic burden upon the freedom and welfare of the genetically programmed ape-men. If this lessens the viability of the ecosystem of ape-men plus cultural organism—the human society—then a competing society may become more viable. The ultimate reality or nature thus selects cultures and genes of systems that better adapt to its requirements.

I am not so much saying anything new about religion as I am explaining its well-known functions in order to make it more credible and understandable in the light of modern science. I feel I am engaged in a task somewhat akin to that of Saint Paul and others, who sought to make the Jesus cult of first-century

Judaism credible in the sophisticated but religiously inadequate Hellenistic culture of the Roman Empire. I marvel that long prior to our new sociobiology he discerned some close parallels. In describing certain functions of good religion, he wrote about two symbiotic natures akin to those I have been describing as essential constituents of each person's life. He called them body and spirit. His words suggest that when these two natures are not suitably coadapted they tend to produce a hellish tension within us. But when we adopt a religious faith that is properly adapted to our creator's requirements and that properly informs us of the true place of our bodily nature in relation to our sociocultural nature, then we are delivered from evil into joyful living.

Likewise, Saint Paul also presented an account similar to the one I have presented here of religion's function to generate voluntary altruism, the miracle of mankind and the "culminating mystery of all biology." Without benefit of our new knowledge, he described the truth of the reality and the power of the closer-than-brotherly love produced by what binds us to one another. He called it our spiritual bond in Christ. I suggest we may scientifically describe this as the common symbiont which has been lodged in each brain that has been enculturated by an equivalent religious culturetype. One could show similar insights from other religions newly credible in the light of sociobiology.

Science and the Progress of Religion in the Future

I have just presented an outline of a small part of the new breakthroughs in scientific understanding and appreciation of the wisdom of ancient and modern religion. And, like Saint Paul speaking to both Greeks and Jews, I, speaking to scientifically informed secularists and to traditional believers, appreciate both and at the same time seek to show that the views of each need to be brought together to yield a larger truth for the more effective communication to all mankind of God's sovereignty, love, and way of salvation.

I see modern science as a new gift of revelation about the not-readily-discernible total reality which is our Creator and the Lord of our History—the larger, environing reality that brought us into being and in which we live and move and have our being. I also find science a more detailed revelation about that tiny part of the larger reality, a part for whose further development and evolution each of us has been given a special awareness and responsibility, but a part whose full meaning, purpose, and hope also are not so readily discernible by unaided common sense. Earlier religions like earlier sciences had different models or images of these hidden realities, which we can now translate for people whose thoughts and feelings on ultimate concerns require confirmation by their more advanced images of the hidden structures of reality. But, as Campbell has noted, the well-winnowed wisdom of ancient religious traditions, apart from their archaic imagery, may be much wiser than narrowly conceived scientific attempts to prescribe human salvation.

I see our task today as similar to that of those who labored some two thousand years ago—following such leaders as Isaiah, the Buddha, Confucius, Socrates, Jesus, and Muhammad—to update our interpretation of the wisdom that a sovereign nature has selected and accumulated in the great world religions so as to adapt it for significance in our radically new context in a world of science and technology. I see the increasingly universally accepted language and imagery of the sciences about human nature, its place in the scheme of things, and the role of religion in human evolution, as now capable (as it was not in the time of Darwin, Marx, and Freud) of providing each of the major religious traditions with the means to interpret and understand itself in harmonious relation with the reality pictures of science and with one another. I see this as leading to the revitalization of religious faith, with an increasingly rational and scientific interpretation, a faith rebinding us to shared goals and mutual caring that enhance life's fulfillment under the requirements and opportunities for humans set by the reality system that is our common creator and sustainer.

2

Potentials for Religion from the Sciences*

While the dominant views of the past century have held that religion is a division of culture inherently divorced from that of the sciences, there have been some who hold that he who has found science in opposition to religion has never properly understood either. While few in number, these have included some of the most distinguished of scientists, if not of theologians, philosophers, humanistic scholars, and poets.[1] Among these there has begun a reexamination of the relevance of the sciences for illuminating human values and religion.

How Can Religion be Defined?

Much contemporary opinion about the nature of religion is such as to make the proposal of a scientific approach to it as ridiculous as Columbus's proposal to sail west to get to the East was to those who believed the world to be flat. Before proposing some of the particular possibilities I have in mind for scientific resources for religion, I should present the picture I hold of the nature of religion which makes it sensible to speak of using the sciences to map its contours.

It would, indeed, be ridiculous if one were to suppose that the sciences would prove that the sun stood still for Joshua;

*This is a revision of a manuscript prepared for the first conference of the Center for Advanced Study in Theology and the Sciences of the Meadville/Lombard Theological School, held in January 1965. Its intent was to summarize some of my earlier proposals concerning the important tasks of such a Center. The paper was first published in *Zygon* 5(2): 110-129, June 1970.

that the gods ruling over human destiny are anthropomorphic ghosts who dwell on the "firmament" conceived of as a platform that holds the waters above the earth; or that we could settle with a microscopic examination just how many angels could stand on the head of a pin.

But the following picture of the nature of religion, which is derived from recent scientific as well as religious scholarship and insight, will make it possible, I hope, to see that the sciences may be as useful for advancing religious theory and for improving religious practice (concerned with the general salvation of man) as they are for medical theory and practice (concerned with human salvation limited primarily to general organic problems).

The meaning of the word "religion," like the meaning of many terms, is defined by its use in language, defined by the way people use it, by the things or behaviors people point to when they use it, by the other words by which they define it. Some words, and "religion" is one of them, have so many different meanings established by many variant forms of use that it is difficult to employ them unambiguously. Such words carry about them a cloud of associated meanings, some of which are so different from others that confusion and disagreement are common. In order to avoid ambiguity and increase the effectiveness of rational discussion, it is customary for scientists to adopt some more logically coherent and limited specification of some commonly observable class of phenomena to which the word or symbol they are using refers. In our proposals for finding scientific resources for religion, it would seem both appropriate and necessary to follow this practice. For religion to come alive in the world of scientific language, it is necessary to use "religion" (and all the related terms that religions use) in the context of scientific language.

I shall, therefore, use a definition of religion that I trust will give it a coherence and relevance in the language of the sciences, yet be faithful to some of its traditional meanings, perhaps to its more significant meanings.

The nature of religion, medicine, and the other arts or techniques under which human cultures thrive can be better understood if we look at them not in terms of the particular practices or ideologies under which they operate in any particular culture or time, but rather in terms of the function or needs which they serve in any or all cultures and times. Much of our trouble with understanding "religion" stems from our narrow identification of its meaning with some specialized characteristics of some particular form of it, perhaps obsolete or irrelevant for us and for those with whom we are communicating. We would have similar problems in discussing transportation if we insisted on fixing our notions of it on canoes or on airplanes. Transportation is defined by neither, and by both, and by much more.

As a matter of fact, the transformation of the role of religion in the cultural evolution from the prescientific to the scientific age is analogous to the parallel transformations of the mechanisms of transportation. The basic functions of religion or transportation, when carefully analyzed, will be seen to be invariant and unchanged, although the specific details of the mechanisms would indeed be different. The analogy is also helpful for our seeing the radically new and radically transformed character of human life which the sciences seem destined to bring to it shortly: the new environment of scientific technology in which we live is as different for personal and social living from pre-industrial agricultural economies as airplanes are from canoes. Without the corresponding transformation of the religious practices and images, men in this new age will not have values that are adequate for the new circumstances of life.

Religion Defined as an Element in Evolving Culture

A useful picture or model of the nature of religion and the other cultural arts or technologies, and their relations to the sciences or ideologies that explain them, can be derived from the historical evolution of the institutions of human society.

In this picture we can view the rites (or behavior patterns) and the myths (or verbal representations of behavior) of religion, medicine, or other technologies, as cultural modifications or extensions that supplement the basic biological processess for sustaining and advancing life. At first the culturally transmitted customs or behaviors were generated not so much by conscious problem solving as by a cultural memory of ways discovered largely by trial and error, and found to be more desirable, useful, viable or salvatory. A solution of some human need had been discovered out of the many largely random trials made by communities of men (or by communities of brain cells in a single man). I do not mean that conscious effort to solve problems was absent, but only that most of the accomplishments of human brains and much of the evolution of human languages, customs, arts, or technologies were not in the past and still are not consciously designed by rational deductions from some already existing valid premises.

Before the rise of systematic and scientific bodies of information, the early evolution of languages, religions, and technologies would seem to be describable as accumulations of know-how and wisdom without human design or plan—that is, so far as human conscious intent is concerned, they were accidental or chance happenings. The successful discoveries or improvements may be said to have been fixed or made a permanent part of human behavior by the genetically established conditioning mechanisms in the nervous systems of individuals, where particular patterns of response were reinforced (selected) by the results of each individual's interactions with other individuals or groups, or with cultural artifacts or with any elements of the larger nonhuman environment. Overall, the retention or selection of these neurologically learned modifications of the genetically based operations for maintaining life through longer periods of time, according to a new notion about cultural evolution which has been greatly stimulated by Sir Julian Huxley and others, is by the relative viability or fitness they bestow on different and competing social groups.[2] In some cases, and always in the end, the failure of organisms to survive will eliminate any unfit class of behavior in organisms.

In this long history or evolution of human culture one can picture the relatively unconscious growth of linguistic structures, religious and medical practices, patterns of social organization, and various technologies for food, clothing, shelter, transportation, communication, manufacture, war, etc. That men were barely conscious of what was transforming their patterns of life in no way detracts from the wisdom or usefulness of the cultural patterns that evolved. Children speak (and their ancestors evolved) languages with a logical grammar long before they become cognizant of logic or grammar.

When the factors providing these cultural modifications of the basic, genetically produced, biological patterns of life-promoting behavior were largely unperceived, explanatory statements of their nature and meaning often did not appear until many generations after the original discoveries took place. At first the explanations were imaginative speculations or plausible myths. It is only recently that we have begun to generate conceptual models or myths that are sufficiently detailed and reliable that they give a very adequate understanding why a sailboat can sail against the wind, why we need to eat sources of vitamin C, how a language came to be, or why death is a necessary good for human progress rather than a meaningless frustration of central values. Many scientists, moreover, feel our best scientific theories are still only plausible myths.

But even before the stage of crude, plausible myths, cultural evolution had much earlier provided implicit know-how or savoir faire. Men are well endowed to "know-how" to do many complicated and useful things long before they can make clearly understandable statements explaining very fully what they are doing—for instance, breathing, digesting food, making babies, cooking food, raising crops, telling the stories of their culture, or spraying DDT. Whether conscious or unconscious, the behavior of living systems is always informed by goals and know-how to accomplish them to maintain life. When this information is incorrect, the living system fails and is no more.

In this picture of cultural evolution (or the historical advance of the socially transmitted know-how of the arts and techniques of human living), the role of consciously manipulable conceptual models and of the breadth of conscious awareness increases in the course of time relative to the role of trial-and-error behavior that is reinforced or selected largely by unconscious genetically programmed neurophysiological mechanisms and by the survival of social institutions.

In the last few centuries, theoretical knowledge or science has become increasingly effective so that, when applied to these traditional arts of life (such as agriculture, communication, medicine, transportation, etc.), the new knowledge has made possible revolutionary advances. In this paper I am suggesting this is also possible for religion. I am suggesting the possibility of a scientifically informed religion, a theology that is congruent with the other modern sciences.

We can summarize that religions, like the other arts and techniques of human culture, have roots in a billion years of genetic evolution and have a history of hundreds of thousands of years of semiconscious cultural evolution; and it was only two or three thousand years ago that they began to advance significantly by the application of conscious, analytical, and deductive reasoning, during the period when the scriptures of the Judaic, Christian, and other great world religions were written. The rational analysis of religious custom and myth (theology) thus began at about the same time as that of history, geography, physics, astronomy, and mathematics.

It can be said that, at whatever the stage of evolution of life, the relation of information (conscious or unconscious) to viable patterns of life is that of hand and glove. Living systems are always informed about their own needs, about the environmental requirements (resources and threats), and about how to behave in this situation to save the living system from death and give it more abundant life.[3]

It seems fair to say that for more than a billion years the functional precursors of science (science being understood as today's best way of gaining valid information) have always been in close alliance with the precursors of religion and the other arts of life. In the light of this history it seems strangely out of place that the dominant opinion of the present learned world should suppose that science and religion were inherently alien and separate from one another after so long being tied together.

I have thus far defined religion by pointing to its reality in human history as one among the arts of human cultures which have evolved to serve some aspect of human needs. But now I should indicate the definition or specification that distinguishes religion from the other arts or techniques of human life.

Religion Defined in Terms of Values

If all the arts of culture serve in some way man's requirements for life, how do we define the particular role of religion?

Theological scholars have suggested that religion is the area of ultimate concern or highest values.

In trying to represent the domain of religion among the complex elements of man's conceptual or verbal structures, we may say that it is possible for man to arrange his concepts of what is valuable in the form of a logical pyramid where the numerous concrete and mundane values are represented in the large area of the base of the pyramid, and the single word or abstract concept that represents man's supreme value is at the highest peak of the pyramid. In such a pyramid there are logical connections structuring the arrangement of elements on each level and also structuring the connections from concrete values at the base to the most general, most abstract, overall value at the top. The several layers of words or ideas near the peak of the pyramid would be the region representing my definition of religion, where we would find words representing comprehensive systems of positive values such as "life."

Going down the logical or verbal pyramid from the peak region of words representing the most sacred, religious values, one would come to levels containing larger networks of terms representing various more particular and concrete expressions of the more general or abstract terms of the layers above. Down a bit toward the base of the pyramid one would, for instance, place such words as "air", "water," "food," "friendship," "honesty," etc., all of them being essential elements for one word in a superior layer, such as "life." And further down toward the base of the pyramid one would find many particular words, where several of them would represent logical equivalents to one of the words or symbols higher in the hierarchy. For instance, related to the logically superior word "food" would be "carbohydrate," "protein," "fat," "vitamin," etc. And below this level one could go down to hundreds of words that represent different sources of "carbohydrate," such as "bread," "potatoes," "cake," and "pie." There would be nothing particularly sacred about "pie" unless in some circumstances it became the only source of the carbohydrate necessary for life.

This reminds us that the priority of values in the lower levels of the value pyramid is circumstantial or situational. The priority of a particular value in a lower plane of the pyramid shifts as the circumstances shift. At one moment "water" may represent a top priority, and at another it may be dangerous or even lethal. But terms representing higher levels in the logical pyramid of values do not shift or change so much with circumstances. Thus "life" remains a very good value word under all kinds of circumstances, and this more abstract value, as the court of appeal for competing, more concrete values of a lower level of the value pyramid will, in conjunction with the existing situation or circumstances, tell us whether water is good or bad or what other lesser value is most important at the moment. It is such words that represent the most general and most invariant and the ultimate values that are associated with and define the area of religious concern.

If, instead of speaking of a logical or subjective hierarchy, we wanted to demonstrate it objectively, we could point out parallels to this logical pyramid of values in living organisms, such that the most sacred or religious area would in fact be concerned with the adaptiveness of the organism to the ultimate requirements of life. For instance, the central nervous system will cut off air (by causing us to hold our breath) when our heads are pushed under water. Thus one rather sacred condition or value for life at a lower level (air) is stopped (for a few moments at least) in order to serve a higher-level value, life itself. Scientists have revealed a complex and marvelous picture of how the animal (including human) organism is given life by means of a complex hierarchy of homeostatic mechanisms, all nicely arranged to order, to repress, or to sacrifice many minor needs in favor of a value more essential for the total system of life. In primitive species, the genetic book, written in the language of DNA, is a primary organizer of behavior to give priority to the needs higher in the pyramid, such as the needs of the total cell or organism. If a certain protein molecule is in too short supply, this organizer will increase its manufacture; and as the number of these molecules reaches an optimum, the organizer will inhibit excessive manufacture.

Even at the level cf organization by DNA, one already finds that the organizer of values rates some values higher than that of the life of the individual cell—the value of the organism; and a value higher than that of the individual organism—that of the species; and (according to some biologists) a value higher than that of the species—that of the total life system in the ecosystem.[4]

In more complex organisms of animals, the DNA has elaborated an assisting mechanism to keep the value hierarchy of the organism such that the higher values of life are served by the way the mechanism orders, restrains, or even sacrifices lesser values. This assisting mechanism is the central nervous system, which serves higher animals as the unifying and ordering center, imposing a hierarchy of priorities on the tremendously complex machinery and operations of the total organism so that each of the millions of the subunits of the organism does just what is necessary for the life of the whole.

In the cultures of human societies, anthropologists have noted that religions have performed the function of societal structuring of value priorities. Religious rites or behaviors and their corresponding myths, ideologies, or theologies, constitute the central cultural institution for the accumulation and transmission of the supreme values in the pyramidal hierarchy of values. Religion relates man to such basic problems as that of life in the face of death, of personal values in conflict with social values, of the relation of man to the ultimate sources and determiners of his destiny—in short, it relates the central values of human life to the total reality upon which that life depends, insofar as an individual's values or goals require social conditioning in addition to the basic accumulation of genetic wisdom.

Ideally, and probably to a large extent in fact in history, all the other social institutions and their characteristic arts or technologies may be said to be integrated into the service of the general goals or values set by the religions. Cultural anthropologists have been clarifying this picture of the centrality of religion for the values of a society. Clyde Kluckhohn said, "Religions have been the traditional repositories of moral values. . . . It is an induction from the evidence at the disposal of the anthropologist that religion in the broad sense is essential to the health and survival of any society. That is, there must be codes which unite individuals in adherence to shared goals that transcend immediate and egocentric interest. There must be intellectually and emotionally acceptable orientations to some of the deeper inevitables such as death."[5]

Another significant anthropological contribution to a scientific understanding of religion is found in a paper entitled "Religious Revitalization: A Function of Religion in Human History and Evolution," by Anthony F. C. Wallace.[6] After reviewing what anthropologists have come up with on the matter of religion, Wallace suggests that this "leads to the view that religious belief and practice always originate in situations of social and cultural stress, and are, in fact, an effort on the part of the stress-laden to construct systems of dogma, myth, and ritual which are internally coherent as well as true descriptions of a world-system, and which thus will serve as guides to efficient action."[7] He then goes on to summarize the essence of the religious process as the effort to discover the essential keys of life—the way to achieve organization, order, or life in the midst of decay and death all around:

the most diverse creeds unite in the attempt to solve the Sphinx-riddle of the relationship between life and death, between organization and disorganization; the ideas of the soul, of gods, of world cycles, of Nirvana, of spiritual salvation and rebirth, of progress—all are formal solutions to this problem, which is indeed felt intimately by all men.

But religion does not offer just any solution: characteristically, it offers a solution which assures the believer that life and organization will win, that death and disorganization will lose.... And religion further attempts to elucidate and describe the organization of self and the cosmos. Religion, then, may be said to be a process of maximizing the quantity of organization in the matrix of perceived human experience.[8]

All the arts of life—including those concerned with food supply, housing and clothing, medicine, manufactures, transport, communication, and government—obviously contribute to producing this maintenance and advancement of life; but religion in human history is seeking to provide solutions to the grand, overall problems, which may be said to lie in the apex of man's pyramid of interrelated needs if he is to live most fully, man's ultimate, most general, and overriding concerns. Religious values interrelate with and provide a general order for all other culturally shaped values. If theology today were the scientific or rational account of the problems or functions of religion in this sense, it might well be called, as it was in the past, the queen of the sciences.

While medicine, agriculture, manufacture, and the other arts of human living contribute to the solution of the various subdepartments of life's needs, the function of religion in this view has historically been the salvation of the whole man in the context of the total reality in which he lives. It attempts to relate us to our ultimate goals and conditions. Having defined religion as an evolving cultural art concerned with the top of our value hierarchy, our problem now is: In the light of the new scientific images of the nature of man and the total reality upon which he is dependent (including his new scientific technologies), what are or should be the overarching values that order his ultimate concerns?

In stable, slowly evolving cultures, we would turn to the traditional religion for this. But, in the middle of the twentieth century, the religions of human culture themselves suffer from a disease of increasing disorder which threatens not only their own continuation but also the continuation of man as a viable species, if an equivalent or more effective guide to the order of the central values of human life is not shortly forthcoming. And without a new form or reformation of religion capable of discerning basic values in the realities revealed by science, man is threatened with the suffocation or lethal absence of the necessary life-giving value structures, just as were fishes which found themselves in the new atmosphere of dried up lakes before they had a chance to evolve adequate mechanisms for taking oxygen from the air. Our suggestion is that the solution of this problem is basically one of finding a rational order for religion which links it to the rational order about reality which the sciences are rapidly developing. Kluckhohn said:

We lack a system of general ideas and values to give meaning to human life in the mid-twentieth century. We live in a period when all of our universals have been challenged.

We can huddle back into the older orthodoxies. We can bear chaos as best we are able and wait for the miracle of a new religion to occur—this is what some of our "wise men" seem to be telling us to do. Or—and this is my thesis—we can bring scientific method and outlook to bear upon these problems. Dewey has warned us "a culture which permits science to destroy traditional values but which distrusts its power to create new ones is destroying itself."[9]

A Way to Relate Religion to Science

The image of "science" for many people may be as much of a problem as their image of "religion," and hence as much of a stumbling block to their viewing with any hope or enthusiasm the supposition that the sciences can be as useful to religion as to medicine. In this section I am not going to try to define science, since I think a scientifically useful definition of this cultural institution for gaining valid knowledge about anything men can know is readily available. But I must reform a no-longer-valid myth about the sciences. Many believe the myth that the sciences can deal only with facts and cannot deal with values. Some of the growing refutation of this myth is found in the above-mentioned paper by Kluckhohn, also in the seven papers of the March 1969 issue of *Zygon,* and in other journals and books.

At the present moment in history, many poets and prophets are so out of touch with the new pictures of the proper nature and meaning of the scientifically validated models or pictures of "reality" and their potential relevance for a new vision of human values and destiny, and so many of the scientific and scholarly world have shut themselves off from serious concern with these problems, that our primary task is to build a new community of minds in which the new knowledge or information about facts in general is directly connected with the basic facts about life's values. This need calls for a return to the relation between fact and values found dominantly in all previous evolution, where the instruments of knowing about self and environment have always been geared to instruments that are genetically informed to provide responses productive of life, that is, geared to the ordering and motivating of the value hierarchy.

We might say that, in this scientific view, the "will" (the motivational program of the central nervous system) is a program of processing information as much as is the "intellect," and that both "values" and "reason" are factual processes or mechanisms investigatable by the sciences. Moreover, in living systems (including human cultures) we find the valuing mechanism tightly geared to the other fact-gathering and analyzing mechanisms. Studies of the brain show this. We properly are frightened at the thought of any further disjunction between the realms of our facts and our values; for natural selection seems to rule that, in any cell, organism, society, or other living system, when the information input about the state of the environment and of the system is not effectively geared to the internal information that structures the values or goals of producing or saving the life of the whole; then neither the information system reporting the state of external affairs nor that registering the internal goal system will survive. Any system of life which is fed and motivated by information that is either erroneous in itself, or inadequately motivating of those responses that are necessary for the viability of the system, would seem to be doomed.

The fear that in our times human culture is undergoing a lethal severing of its value system from its general information system has been increasingly sounded as an alarm by great artistic and scholarly observers of the human condition in the past century. Leaders from both sides of this lethal schizophrenia of our culture must find ways to tie them together. This defines the task of a center for the study of how religion (as I have defined it) may grow and prosper in the light of the sciences.

I do not view the general method of research in this approach to religious or theological problems through the sciences as being primarily a matter of employing the scientific method at the empirical, testing level to develop new science, at least not for the near future. It would seem more fruitful to consider our problem as one of applying the already scientifically validated conceptual models of "reality" (including the reality of values) to the problems of religion. In this sense, religious science (theology), like medical science, would be primarily an area of applied science. The area of the applied science in each case is defined by the traditional problems of human salvation or therapy in religion or medicine. When any relevant information already existing in any of the sciences is brought to bear upon the solution of such religious or medical needs, we have an example of "applied science."

For religion this does not necessarily mean that all of the more ancient religious ideas and practices will be cast aside. In my opinion much of these more ancient formulas for salvation, both genetic and cultural, still today constitute a significantly valid core in medicine as well as in religion, and will only gradually shift with further evolution. This is particularly clear in medicine, where even the precultural wisdom of the body or the genotype is so far ahead of any synthetic wisdom of medical science that we would not survive a minute without it. And so far as modern scientific medical theory and practice are concerned, there are those who have questioned whether the negative impacts of medical care on the human gene pool are not more deleterious than all the temporary relief it has provided. It should be clear that modern science may be a rather feeble light so far as overall and long-range human values are concerned, even at the level of medical health and genetics. But, granting that, the present crisis in human values, combined with the new potentials of the sciences for helping man to understand, advance, and reinforce his values at the most sacred levels of religion as well as at the level of medicine, constrains us to examine how the various sciences might contribute to the rise of a more effective modern religion.

The solutions to religious problems—man's ultimate hopes and fears, his supreme values, the basic purposes or meaning of his life, his proper attitudes and responses to his fellowmen and to the ultimate realities upon which his destiny depends—are, like solutions to problems of medical health, partially supplied by the following three sources of wisdom: genotypic, organic, and anciently evolved cultural formulas. A fourth source is applied science. Although the sciences have been applied more quickly to other cultural arts, I suspect that man's capacity to survive depends on his success in finding a new, rational, and scientific illumination and ordering of these religious problems now even more than problems of medicine, politics, economics, or any of the other arts of living. It is my belief that the wealth of information in the contemporary sciences about the nature of human life and the conditions or requirements imposed by the realities upon which it depends offer the best hope to those who would seek viable answers to these problems of man's ultimate concerns or values. Even if this proposal to translate and strengthen religious values in the light of the sciences seems to be but a wild dream, it may deserve serious effort just because nothing more sensible is being done to stop the increasing moral, emotional, and social disorder of our times which threatens man's continued viability. Even random attempts to resolve the problem are clearly better than no attempts, as the billion-year history of evolving life indicates.

We may have to learn to breathe values in the new atmosphere of science or else we may suffocate and perish from the face of the earth. I turn now to some of the religious problems where I think the sciences offer rich resources.

Agenda for the Development of Theology in the Light of the Sciences

The remainder of this chapter was originally written to indicate the broad range of theological questions for which the sciences may have some significant new information, and thus includes topics beyond those which are developed in this book. Therefore, it might now be skipped and returned to after reading chapters 3-7. This "Agenda" section would then constitute an appendix outlining a wider range of further topics ready for related development toward a theology that is more credible and hence effective because it is true in the light of the sciences and yet also faithful to the ultimate concerns of religion because of new truth about those concerns.

In the following section I present some of the religious questions or problems for which I think the sciences already have or soon may provide new insights and help, either to confirm ancient religious insights and make them more effective in today's conditions of life, or to revise or reform them to this same end. This is an agenda for scientists and theologians in collaboration.

Although these areas and the questions under them are largely expressed in language relating them to the conceptual schemes of the sciences and the philosophy of science, and are somewhat unorthodox for theological jargon, a careful reading will reveal some of the primary areas of traditional theological doctrine.

1. *The Sources of Valid Information—Especially about Basic Human Values.* The problem of truth or validity has always been a major concern of religion and these epistemological problems are among the most critical for contemporary theology. Two major questions are: How is valid information about himself, the world, and the paths to life revealed to man?

How is knowledge of right and wrong (values) converted into right behavior?

Among the areas of the sciences which may be fruitful for this exploration are the following: *(a)* the new epistemology which has grown primarily out of the physical sciences, one which has given man a powerful tool for acquiring new truth much more rapidly and surely than the older processes of reason, tradition, and intuition; *(b)* the psychological (including behavioral and neurophysiological) pictures of the nature of learning and knowing, and of the neurophysiological ties linking information to feeling and behaving; *(c)* the social science pictures of the evolution of social traditions of know-how and of conceptual images or models of reality; *(d)* the general biophysical pictures of cybernetics, dynamic homeo-stasis, and information theory showing a relation between life, order, and information, including the cumulative, natural selec-tion of better-adapted forms and transmission of their succes-sions of increasingly ordered codes of information about how to live and to live more abundantly.

While area *a* in the above paragraph taken by itself has had a history of constant warfare with many theological traditions, it has great significance for theologians who are concerned with credibility and validity. The inclusion of the other three areas makes room for such religiously fertile concepts as "life-giving wisdom accumulated in cultural traditions, far beyond the power of any single generation to build up from scratch," and "life-giving information accumulated in genotypic and phenotypic structures." Areas *b, c,* and *d* also provide the close tie between science and values, which in the light of area *a* alone has often been erroneously asserted to be nonexistent. The pictures in areas *b–d* would further seem to provide important new clues for that ancient problem of theology—the relation of knowing to behaving—in words ascribed to Saint Paul: Why do I do that which I would not, and fail to do that which I would? Taking all four areas together, there would seem to be a rich harvest for understanding the nature, source, validity, and improvement of man's knowledge about those things which are of ultimate concern for human life or ultimate values of life. There are grounds for new understandings of the nature and validity of mystic experiences and of the dynamics involved in the sifting or selection of the sacred rituals, beliefs, and literature of a culture. There is enough material in this general area alone for a major transformation and growth of theology.

2. *Toward an Enlarged Doctrine of Man.* From earliest religious myths to the most recent theologies, the basic values inherent in human life have been pictured as something more enduring and significant than meets the eye of casual observation. Similarly, the contemporary scientific pictures of man, showing him to be the product of cosmic forces operating in stellar and planetary evolution which give rise to living organisms up through human societies, would seem to be a rich source for extending the validity and range of man's notions of the enduring role and values of his nature in the cosmic scheme of evolving life; of his vital relation to the cosmic powers that ordain his life; and of his consequent meaning, his destiny and duties, and his hope for the salvation of his ultimate values thereunder. Perhaps the greater richness of this new revelation of the source and destiny of man is proportional to the million-fold extension of the time span of the familiar biblical story of a few thousand years from the creation until today to the few billion of contemporary evolutionary theory.

The sciences provide rich new information on such questions as: What is man? What is this wonderful, invisible "soul" or invisible and persisting "spirit" of human values inscribed in a DNA code, so comprehensive for directing life and yet so small that the complete DNA details for generating all of the approximately three billion existing different human forms could be held in one hand? What are the essential elements and values of individual life behavior in this context? How do these elements and values find continuity to survive and evolve through millennia of time? What novel characteristics did the creative processes of evolution bestow upon man that made him unique and in some senses supreme among all creatures of the earth?

In what ways and to what degree has man been endowed with the powers and the responsibilities for consciously aiding the creative processes of advancing life on earth? How did man's discovery of the tree of knowledge (which was genetically provided by an expanded neocortex of the brain and by nongenetic storage and transmission of learning by culture) present him with the agonizing consciousness of this fate: to labor consciously all his days to seek the good and shun the evil and yet inevitably to suffer evil and die? Why are suffering and death necessary for the evolution of life? What vital and core elements of human nature persist beyond death, other than the genotype? In what sense is motivation of the individual to self-sacrificing behavior for the welfare of the extended family, of the local society, and ultimately of the whole species and even the total ecology of life a value incorporated in the genotype and phenotype, incarnate in the motivational mechanisms of the central neuroendocrine systems, in the socially transmitted mores and moral codes? How are men (and animals) motivated to perform and to find pleasures even in activities seen to be destructive or lethal to the organism but which are beneficial for the gene pool of the species or for the survival and welfare of the local society? What may this imply for the cultural amplifications of the same general types of behavior?

How may we today conceive of the central core of the system of realities which constitute the central values of life-producing structures and events in man? To what extent do they extend beyond the concrete and relatively temporary pattern of particular atomic particles, molecules, cells, organs, organisms, societies, and even species that constitute mankind? To what extent does man's reality and meaning lie in his society, species, or ecosystem? How far can one describe the value-increasing or enhancing direction of life and human life in terms of the search (random or guided) toward increasing levels of order, organization, or dynamic homeostasis? How far can "order" and life be related to the notion of entropy consumption suggested by Schrödinger in his *What Is Life?* To the extent that we can clarify scientifically man's central values, how far can we go in a self-conscious program to enhance the life of man in the various aspects of his nature: genetic (in a program of eugenics), personal (in a program of cultural shaping by education of the phenotype), and social (in a program of improving the life-sustaining and enhancing structures and functions of the community of men within the ecosystem)?

Why are men created so differently from one another, such that some may be more successful under some conditions and less successful under others (genetic and cultural polymorphism)? Why should we suspect there may be virtues hidden in the most unlikely and sometimes seemingly abhorrent characteristics of ourselves and other men (i.e., the values of polymorphism)? What new insights do the sciences provide on human predestination or determinism and freedom or responsibility?

In terms of contemporary sciences, how should we understand the meaning of such terms as "mind" and "body"? What is the meaning of the fact that certain behavioral scientists claim there is no such thing as "mind" and certain physical scientists claim there is no "body" outside of those that are experiences or phenomena of the "mind" and some scientists allow for the usefulness of both terms "mind" and "body" or their equivalents? Have some scientists or semanticists provided some clarification of the meanings of these terms and a reduction of the paradoxes they have led us into? Within the conceptual schemes of the basic sciences, what meanings can we assign to terms like "self," "person," "personality," etc.? What about "soul," "spirit"? Can the meanings of these terms be related to the more basic science pictures of man as "organism"? Are there in man two independent systems of reality? If so, do they interact in any way? Is careful, scientific use of language a solution to the paradoxes that arise out of certain terms used in trying to describe aspects of human nature?

All the sciences—physical, biological and psychosocial—would seem to contain the materials for a greatly enriched and more valid story of the genesis, nature, destiny, and hope of man.

3. *Toward a Richer Doctrine of the Realities on Which Man's Life Depends.* Religions have long pictured or formulated the ultimate sources of events determining human destiny in symbols of superhuman, often invisible, entities: spirits or gods. A most significant opportunity may await an imaginative attempt to formulate the ultimate ground, source, and determination of human destiny in terms of the rich new pictures of the sciences. To what extent can this source be formulated as a single,

universal, interconnected whole? Is the totality of all things and events (the cosmos) in some sense interrelated, one and single? Or, is there more than one separate and independent system of reality and power? Is there a basic discontinuity between the determinants or the laws governing biological and those governing social behavior? Is there a mental or psychic world that is independent of other things? What other things are there which are not aspects of direct perception?

How does man know about the realities which create, sustain, and enrich his life? To what extent is man integrated with and a part of the total reality upon which his life depends? Are the values of the open systems or islands of order or life (decreasing entropy) on earth (or other planets in the cosmos) definitely doomed ultimately by the heat-death hypothesis? Is the cosmos a closed system? Whence came the lower entropy of earlier states of the system? Is there no escape from the fear of the triumph of death over life? Are there escapes by valid transformations of our conceptual models of who we are? Is there any escape or any reason to seek escape from the ultimate power of the cosmic system in which we find ourselves?

Can man define his own heaven and achieve it regardless of the cosmic circumstances and laws? Or, is he forced to bow before some objective reality or realities which say what he may (and what he may not) do if he is to have life, and life more abundant? What then is his proper attitude and response to such a reality? To what extent did, does, and will man's life depend on his adaptation of his own will to the conditions required by the realities of his environment? Is there any limit to the capacity of living systems, including men, in seeking, finding, and incorporating (or adapting to) ever more fully the elements of the objective reality on which his life and its further progress depends? Are there grounds in the scientific pictures of man and the reality that made him and determines his destiny which would lead man to rejoice and possess hope and courage under the events of our times? Are there reasons to stand in awe of the program of creative evolution, to praise its wonder and glory, to be grateful for the grace that has brought us into being and set before us a responsibility for the maintenance and advancement of life?

What is man's proper attitude to this course of his life? Is it to be feared? Is it to be loved? Is it to be respected? In the scientific world view: What is sacred? What is holy? What is required? What are the commandments? What is grace? Is the source of life objectively independent and unchangeable, or can man in some way change it? By magic? By persuasion? By petition? If the scientifically portrayed cosmos or ultimate ecosystem, as it evolves in time and spreads out life (including man) to cover the face of the earth, is that on which man's life depends, and if the cosmic unfolding is ultimately independent of anything that man can do to change it, does man have any recourse but submission to the requirements for life thereby laid down? What can the terms "freedom" and "responsibility" mean in such a world view? Do the modern sciences offer any better answers than the theological concepts of "predeterminism," "fate," "destiny," "wheel of life"? Can the scientific picture of man's place in the system be translated so as to lead man to feelings of security, salvation, joy, even ecstasy?

4. *Revised Visions of Human Goals and Hopes.* What can the religious term "salvation" mean in the light of the sciences? Is it pleasure? Is it life? Life more abundant? To what extent is it a gift of forces beyond human ken? To what extent may or must man act consciously to achieve it; what requirements are placed upon man to achieve it?

How can meaningful salvation for an individual be made sensible in the face of the denial of happiness or fulfillment by such seeming evils as disabilities and insanities produced *(a)* by the genotype, *(b)* by inadvertent environmental events, *(c)* by inadvertent social accidents, *(d)* by social injustices, *(e)* by social necessities, *(f)* by inevitable death (sometimes prematurely) of each organism and species?

To what extent is the welfare of the society necessarily incompatible with the welfare of the individual? Are life and life's achievements ultimately doomed by the nature of the cosmos? How can knowledge or truth about what can cause man to flourish become dynamic in moving him to behave accordingly? How do individual needs find suitable integration with those of society? What is the ideal or optimal solution for the system containing individual and society?

Is it possible in the light of the sciences to say anything about man's goals, purposes, meaning, function, or role in the cosmic scheme of things? What are the contributions beyond those already suggested?

5. *Some Implications for the Nature of Future Institutions Which Transmit Basic Human Values.*   Do the psychosocial or other sciences provide new insights into the role of social or cultural institutions in providing men with better information and motivation for higher values and attaining more abundant life? In this light, and in the light of the previous theological inquiries, what kinds of institutions can we envisage for optimum effectiveness in improving and propagating human values? How are values imparted, taught? To what extent is or should the church (or its successor) be an educational institution? What is the role of doctrine in the imparting of values and the corresponding behaviors and feelings? What is the role of artistic and aesthetic rituals or devices such as incense, music, bodily motions, architecture, drama, images, etc.? What are the roles of the members of a religious community in relation to one another? What sanctions or behavioral-pattern reinforcers does or can the church have for its moral and other teachings?

To what extent is a pluralism of religious institutions desirable? What institutions that do not commonly go under the name "Religious" are in fact performing traditional religious functions such as transmitting the central values of the society, salving the anxieties and agonies of people, educating people to realise their highest potentials, etc.? What new "religious" institutions have arisen outside the formally recognized churches? To what extent are television, psychotherapy, communism, etc., religious in their impact? How independent should the church be from the state and from other institutions of the society? To what extent is it desirable for local religious institutions to be tied to other bodies and to be tied to a hierarchy of regional, national, or worldwide leadership for supplying guidance or control of forms, instruments, literature, education, etc.?

To what extent is a new holy scripture called for? Is Henry Alexander Murray's[10] call for a new Bible based on world literature of all cultures and of recent as well as ancient sources, of science as well as drama, called for? What can be suggested for motivation and emotional satisfaction in view of recent discoveries of the organic relation between information and feeling and behavior? How can the scientific portrayal of the drama of man's history and his destiny be made more effective? Can it provide a resolution to conflicting sacred dogmas and cultures through reason, evidence, and persuasion instead of by warfare? Can it provide clarity and enthusiasm where there is confusion and apathy? To what extent does the present human genotype limit the development of any necessary tolerance, reason, cooperation, or altruism? Do we need to and how should we alter the characteristics of the gene pool in order for man to improve or to continue in being? Are there as yet unused means of transforming and civilizing the phenotypic outcome of the genotype by better environmental forces, conditioning procedures, reinforcement programs, educational methods, etc.? Can we do these things in time?

Coda

The above are only samples of basically religious questions where the various sciences offer a wealth of recent information for clarification and for the building of new or reformed models or concepts. Theologians and men charged with the "propagation of the faith" of whatever present tradition from Confucian to Communist and from Hindu to Hebrew and Christian can restate them in their own languages. It is urgent that this task be undertaken now, if it is in fact the case that man is gasping for spiritual breath of life as he is evolving into a new culture dominated by science and technology.

But the above samples of the theological questions where modern science could help give better answers are primarily valid for theoretic ordering or models of the realities of religious concern. Even if a clear, orderly, and valid theoretic picture could be produced, we are still a long way from producing that necessary element of religion or medicine called the "rituals" or "clinical practices," the actual behaviors that are effective for delivering men from evil. Before any theory (including theology) can be usefully applied to basic human needs or values, it must be transformed into simple formulas that can be successfully performed by any man or child, such as pushing the button, taking the pill, or singing the song. The complex concepts underlying television, medication, or man's ultimate good have to be translated into forms and procedures effectively usable by children. We have promises to keep and miles to go before we sleep.

NOTES

1. The authors and literature cited in *Zygon* provide a sample.
2. See Ralph Wendell Burhoe, "Five Steps in the Evolution of Man's Knowledge of Good and Evil," chap. 3 in this book, originally in *Zygon* 2 (1967):82–83, esp. n. 28.
3. See n. 2 above and Ralph Wendell Burhoe, "Values via Science," *Zygon* 4 (1969):65–99.
4. See, for instance, Alfred E. Emerson, "Dynamic Homeostasis: A Unifying Principle in Organic, Social, and Ethical Evolution," *Zygon* 3 (1968):129–68, esp. p. 157.
5. Clyde Kluckhohn, "The Scientific Study of Values and Contemporary Civilization," *Proceedings of the American Philosophical Society* 102 (1958):470; reprinted in *Zygon* 1 (1966):232.
6. Anthony F. C. Wallace, "Religious Revitalization: A Function of Religion in Human History and Evolution," presented at the 1961 summer conference of the Institute on Religion in an Age of Science and published separately by the Institute; later published in Anthony F. C. Wallace, *Religion: An Anthropological View* (New York: Random House, 1966).
7. Wallace, *Religion,* p. 30.
8. Ibid., pp. 38–39.
9. Kluckhohn, "Scientific Study of Values," p. 470 (in *Proceedings*); p. 233 (in *Zygon*).
10. Henry Alexander Murray, "A Mythology for Grownups," *Saturday Review,* January 23, 1960, pp. 9, 11–12.

3

Five Steps in the Evolution of Man's Knowledge of Good and Evil*

At our Star Island conferences of the Institute on Religion in an Age of Science, for more than a decade we have been wrestling off and on with a scientific approach to understanding right and wrong or good and evil. For the most part we have been asking scientists of various kinds to say what they think their understanding of the scientific pictures of things may imply for human values and religion. At the close of this year's conference, on how man can know right from wrong, I shall try to draw together elements from a number of our papers this year and from past years, as well as from other sources in the sciences, to make what seems to me a coherent picture of man's long history of learning to distinguish good from evil.

First, I wish to assert that the pictures of man and the world, on which we are basing our analysis, are the pictures currently widespread among leaders in various fields of science. These conferences on religion in an age of science have not been based on esoteric fringes of the scientific community but have involved scientists near what might be described as the top center of recent scientific development in several fields. I cite a sampling of publications to designate what I mean by top center of recent scientific mappings of man and his world relevant to our problem of the relation of science to values, a

*This is a revision of a paper for the 1965 conference of the Institute on Religion in an Age of Science on: How Can Man Know Right from Wrong? Experts from several disciplines contributed to the conference and their full papers, which are referred to here, can be found in *Zygon* 2(1), March 1967, where this chapter was first published on pages 77–96.

sample which, perhaps, exaggerates a little the frequency of IRAS conference participants.[1]

Also, I should note that scientists here have used the terms "good and evil" and "right and wrong" loosely. We have not always reflected the special meaning of these terms in religion and theology, nor have we even been consistent among ourselves. I don't think this makes too much difference in our initial essays to apply the sciences to the problems of religion, a task that is so unconventional and difficult that I think we shall be forgiven for some present inconsistencies.

A Scientific Revelation of Primary or Intrinsic Value

By and large, I would say that we have all been referring to a single, common, primary value, life, and this in the context of an evolutionary picture on which there is a great consensus among us. From this primary value of evolving life, all our other values are derived as means or ways to this end. We all seem agreed that the sciences are a fertile source of revelation of the nature of these secondary values serving viability. Some of us go further to argue that we cannot help ourselves in adopting "life" as the primary, or, as the philosophers would say, the "intrinsic," value relative to which other values are "instrumental."

In this evolutionary scheme of life, some of us have limited our notions of human values to those values that emerge only after man emerges from the animal to the human societal and cultural level. But others of us would rather stress the continuity of values through all levels of emerging life, from the events preceding nature's first selection of certain patterns of self-replicating complex molecules to man and beyond to man's successors. Either definition is proper so long as the speaker makes clear the different semantic limits or bounds within which he is using the term. It is perfectly proper to limit the denotation of "human" and "human values" to those aspects of man that emerged only after the date we find for the emergence of *Homo sapiens*. But, as everyone knows, man still has in his genotype a vast heritage whose origins contemporary comparative biochemistry traces back in some cases to the time when yeasts emerged and even beyond.[2] These genotypic patterns encode and specify basic values of the human being to which, so long as they remain, all subsequently evolved refinements and restructuring of values must conform. Hence such ancient values are still a determinative ground for all contemporary values, even of the highest human cultures. Therefore, I wish to make it clear that I am describing human values in the wider framework of time and events of the cosmos as they are manifest in scientific revelations concerning the total evolution of life on earth. I take this larger frame of reference in order to embrace the scientific revelations that bring us as close as I think we can come to understanding the cosmic source of our "ultimate," "intrinsic," "most sacred," or "religious" values.

I shall describe this revelation of the sciences concerning man's ultimate or intrinsic values simply by pointing to a notion that has been established only in the past two or three decades since A. I. Oparin[3] first suggested the billions of years of molecular evolution leading up to what we now call living forms, and the notion set forth by Erwin Schrödinger[4] and Norbert Wiener[5] that this whole process can be distinguished very nicely by the fact that it is a program that runs exactly counter to the general or most probable program of the surrounding environment. That is, evolving life is the growth of organization or order which represents a decrease in entropy in a world that in general operates under the second law of thermodynamics in the direction of increasing entropy or increasing disorder. One must quickly add that life does not violate the second law, but, as Schrödinger pointed out, a living organism has the "astonishing gift of concentrating a 'stream of order' on itself and thus escaping the decay into atomic chaos—of 'drinking orderliness' from a suitable environment."[6]

One must also point out that this character of living organisms is the product of a "natural selection" by the environment. As Oparin states, in describing the dynamics of directed chemical evolution of molecular aggregations (including collodial gels or coazervates), "Of course, the mere gain in dynamic force and the acceleration of chemical reactions within the coazervate could not determine the further evolution of such formations, but the increasing rate of chemical transformation was all the time regulated by a 'natural selection' of newly arising formations. If the increase in the rate of a given reaction so affected the coördination between assimilation and degradation as to promote the latter, such an imperfect system would become mechanically unfitting for further evolution and would perish prematurely."[7]

I would summarize this revelation of the sciences as saying that life is a system of order maintained in an environment that ordinarily decreases order and that the primary direction, goal, or value of life, which was established by the natural selection that is an inherent characteristic of the general environment, is to continue that order or, in the history of evolutionary development, to increase that order. Here I think we have a definition of the primary, intrinsic, or ultimate goal or value of any living system, a definition established by the nature of the cosmos itself in creating living systems. Any act of a living system that violates this primary value simply weeds out that living system. Hence all living systems possess this cardinal or inherent value. One could say that life was created by, and its primary goal or value is forever established by, the nature of the cosmos. The various subsidiary goals or routes to this intrinsic value are legion, but not infinite. It is the task of all evolving systems of life to explore further routes to this primary goal as challenged by the ever changing circumstances set forth by the environment. To do otherwise is to lose all value as a living system.

The question of how long this primary value of life will be maintained by the cosmos is not clearly settled by the scientific pictures. Some, such as Bertrand Russell or Wiener,[8] who believe that the total cosmos is forever operating according to the second law of thermodynamics, find themselves compelled to predict the eventual end of life in the heat death of such a cosmos. But these people give no account of the origin of the available energy of the cosmos, and there are related problems that the sciences cannot now or perhaps ever definitively answer. In any case, man finds himself in the midst of this order-building program in a system that appears capable of sustaining itself billions of years into the future, and it seems to me quite enough for our worries and hopes that we live in the confident faith that this is our goal for much farther in the future than we can reasonably see. No doubt at some time, perhaps in a year, perhaps in a million, we will find some better resolution of our role in the distant future of billions of years hence. Meanwhile entropy remains a problem for theodicy.

Anthropologist Anthony F. C. Wallace pointed out at our IRAS conference in 1961, in summarizing the essence of an estimated one hundred thousand varities of religions in human cultural evolution, that "this dialectic, the 'struggle' (to use an easy metaphor) between entropy and organization, is what religion is all about."[9] A wide scientific community seems to see this negentropic or order-building goal as the primary good or value of life, running as a common thread from the primitive organic chemicals to the highest religions.

In this paper I wish to bring together in review, for the better understanding of our problem, "how man can know right from wrong," some of the subsidiary mechanisms that operate under this ultimate value of any living system to inform man concerning what is good or right.

Five Steps in Learning to Know Right from Wrong

As I see it, the sciences reveal five steps in man's history of learning to know right from wrong and good from evil. These steps represent what in the language of evolutionary theory are called emergent levels of novel systems of life. At these Star Island conferences we have heard many scientists, such as Hudson Hoagland,[10] Harlow Shapley,[11] and Oscar Riddle,[12] talk about these emergent forms or new structures of reality that appear when the lower forms are organized in special ways. I shall outline in brief five major steps in a series of evolutionary emergents, that is, five successive and important ways by which man is able to distinguish right from wrong.

1. *Genotypic knowledge.* The first step is genetic learning. Oparin, and Hoagland among others at this conference, have told us about the more than a billion years of genetic learning about what is right if we are to have life. More than three decades ago Walter B. Cannon[13] wrote of "the wisdom of the body"—describing some of the wonderful bodily mechanisms that carry on billions of operations in each of us in such a complex and elaborate way that no one could consciously

operate the system. Present biology strongly suggests that these mechanisms develop as our bodies grow under the guidance of patterns "learned' or "selected" in the phylogeny or development of the human genotype over millions of years. Many scientists at these IRAS conferences—Theodosius Dobzhansky,[14] Alfred Emerson,[15] R. W. Gerard,[16] Hudson Hoagland,[17] A. G. Huntsman,[18] Ashley Montagu,[19] H. A. Murray,[20] George Wald,[21] and others—have told us how our loves, hates, and basic values, are grounded in our genetic heritage. In prehuman animals it is known that the genotype is the primary code that directs sometimes complex co-operative social behavior;[22] in man, the genotype is only a necessary foundation for moral and social behavior. Robert Morison has pointed out one way that this genetic code for knowing what is good still operates at the human level: "individual self-sacrifice for the good of the community . . . is built into the material roots of his biological system."[23] Cultural anthropologists have joined the biologists in recognizing the genetic code of values as undergirding all human values. Ward Goodenough told us that in goal- or value-directed behavior "the genes provide the foundation."[24] Since there are perhaps ten billion "words" in the human genotype, a truly huge encyclopedia of information about what is right and wrong, I have sometimes called this the ten billion commandments in contrast to Moses' ten.

2. *The brain's knowledge.*   The second great step for discerning good and bad emerged when multicellular animal organisms began to elaborate special cells and organs of cells that we call the central nervous system. Dr. Hoagland also outlined how this new (emerging especially rapidly in the past million years) instrument of knowing good and evil operates.[25] While its basic structure is patterned by the genotype, the brain operates at a new level of learning and keeps in its memory not only the wisdom of racial history incorporated in the genotype but also many new pieces of information about what is good and bad, learned in the development of the individual from birth till death. He pointed out how the RNA molecules, so similar to the DNA letters of the genetic code, may be the alphabet in which the brain's memory is written. And he noted how this instrument of life, of survival—the brain—functions to

provide values, to integrate the information fed to it into a hierarchy of values, relating this information to genetically established centers of "pain and pleasure" in the lower brain, which direct our choices so as to maximize the possibilities for life.

This organ in man, with its great freedom to make the investigations and choices, brings upon man the terrible burden of the conscious knowledge of good and evil. Some of our IRAS scientists, such as Dobzhansky, have told us how akin this is to the story in Genesis about man's eating from the tree of knowledge and becoming aware of good and evil.[26] The social life of the insects is directed almost completely by the genotypic code of right and wrong, their brains being too small to provide for the complex mechanisms of consciousness and culture; and hence insects do not have, nor do they require for their level of life, the knowledge that weighs on the minds of men with the uncertainties and anxieties about the future.[27]

3. *Culturally transmitted knowledge.* The third step in emergent evolution of mechanisms for distinguishing between good and evil appeared only in the past few million years when there evolved a central nervous system complex enough to communicate information or knowledge from one organism to another for many generations without sending it through the genetic language. This occurs to some degree in many— perhaps most—animal species but does not become very significant until we reach the hominids and man. In us the development of the brain and related organs of communication makes possible the transmission of a symbolic code of information not only from parent to child but from maiden aunt to child and from dead men to strangers of another culture and century.

Ward Goodenough has told us how, with the development of social specialization and interdependence, codes of right and wrong developed which, though requiring that the individual give and take on his immediately sensed, genetically structured values of good and bad, on the whole added new information that tended to optimize *both* individual and social opportunities for life. The human brain's new ways of learning and new ways of storing information now become part of the

machinery for the evolution and storage of social information—information that can be transmitted to the community in
seconds instead of centuries. The knowledge of good and bad
to be transmitted may be said to have been selected (and
sacralized) by its capacity to promote survival, whether or not
the mechanism of selection is consciously perceived. Such
knowledge becomes embedded in the "culturetype" (the
myths, language, technology, and characteristic social
behavior) of the society largely, it may be presumed, because it
was sacred for the viability of the society. The culturetype is,
then, a joint product of the genotype and the environment,
which is fed back to each new generation of the society. The
culturetype thus becomes a new source of information, a
relatively stable and transmittable "heritage" in addition to the
genotype, but with considerable independence from the
genotype. Living sociocultural organisms are the sites where
responses to the environment are organized under the heritage
of more or less stable information, which has been provided
jointly by genotype and culturetype. The waxing and waning of
populations with particular characteristics is the "natural selection" of the information heritages which they incarnate.
Related notions will be found set forth, not yet in fully harmonious fashion, by scientists whose works I have cited.[28]

Co-operating with natural selection, cultures also consciously developed new ways of motivating their behavioral
codes through socially imposed sanctions, although, as Ward
Goodenough pointed out, no cultural code can violate the
internal codes of good and evil in each organism established by
the genotype. The religious traditions that evolved in different
primitive cultures were, like languages, semiconsciously
accrued bodies of wisdom with various functions to provide
man with courage, hope, fear, and other adaptive attitudes or
feelings toward the often invisible forces in his environment,
which, like weather, disease, and animals, represented hopes or
threats to his felt needs.[29]

Proper or responsible behavior for the welfare of the more
discernible fellowmen seems to have been a later development
of religions to facilitate or sanction the individual's acceptance
of the established moral codes and to some extent to help
formulate or reform the moral code itself for greater viability

of the group. (The genetic code of values took care of this earlier.) In most societies most of the moral code is not enforcible to any great extent by police or socially enforced power but is primarily maintained by internalizing the social values in the central nervous system as a conscience or superego, reinforced by religious beliefs and social sanctions.[30] As Ward Goodenough indicated, the superpersonal forces, superior to men and called gods, became the source of the sanctions, the hopes and fears, that enforce the moral code.

4. *Rational knowledge.* The fourth step in the emergent evolution of new mechanisms for knowing good from evil and right from wrong is a cultural development that is intermediate between the primitive cultural mechanisms of step 3 and the modern sciences which I am calling step 5. This fourth step has been dominant in the the higher human civilizations of the past three thousand years. An understanding of the mechanism underlying this fourth step will help us understand some of the virtues and weaknesses of traditional theology and philosophy as guides to knowledge of right and wrong and will also help us to understand the nature of the fifth step, science.

The fourth step may be called logic, reason, or rationality. This arose in large measure by the discovery of the logical powers of language as a means of finding truth and for helping to resolve life's perplexing ambiguities. The Greeks, in our cultural tradition, discovered how the predicting or projecting processes of the brain could, by using as an input the partial model of the events of the world and their relations found symbolically represented in language, compute new truth, test it, and to a remarkable degree "prove" whether it is right or wrong, whether the problem was one of geometry or ethics.

These powers of language originally evolved by a largely unconscious selection in human behavioral patterns. But, when linguistic symbols and rules of usage (grammar, etc.) are used, they provide a newly emergent mechanism for what we call the process of conscious reasoning or rationality. The unconsciously evolved structure of language provides a highly abstracted and useful model of the world evolved in the selection of phenotypic behavior patterns encoded in the memory machinery of the brain. Its structure provides some capacity to deduce new knowledge by operating under its rules. We call this logical deduction. According to some philosophers of science, this is the ground on which modern science is built.

Most of us today are familiar with the grounds of logic. We know that if you can say two things you may have the power to be convinced of the truth of a third and new thing as a consequence. (1) All men are mortal; (2) Socrates is a man; (3) hence Socrates is mortal.

To illustrate the connection between a logically operated symbolic system or language and what we now call science, we can look at that ancient but still largely valid special language we call geometry. The Euclidean geometry was a system of symbols representative of the space of experience and the rules for manipulating them to produce new information. For instance, every high-school graduate knows that the Euclidean language about triangles tells us that, if we can measure only three parts of a triangle, we can logically deduce the correct or true lengths or angles of three other hitherto unknown parts.

Especially in this area of geometry, the Greeks may be said to have discovered the basic elements of our fifth step, science. From their symbolic models of triangles the Greeks knew how to deduce accurately the width of a river without ever crossing the river. They needed only to measure a length between two points on one side of the river and the angles formed as they made a line of sight from each end of that line to a single point on the other side of the river. A high point in the power of geometric language was the Greek measurement of the circumference of the earth with only a small error, nearly two thousand years before Magellan sailed around it. This they did by measuring the length of the shadows of two sticks at two points along the Nile River in Egypt.

This same logical power of language was used in the development of religious, theological, and moral ideas. The Greek philosophers used the same power of language to develop their ethics, and at the same time the writers and editors of the Old and New Testaments were using it (some say with less rigor of internal coherence than the Greeks but with more effort to test against history or empirical experience) in their development of religious ideas. The early Christian theologians took upon themselves the task of making logical and rational interpretations about the Judaic pictures of God, man, and his salvation to the best of their ability under the canons of logic established by the Greeks. This resulted in a beautiful culmination of rational interpretation of Christian doctrine, such as that by Thomas Aquinas.

5. *Scientific knowledge.* Wonderful as were the geometrics, philosophies, and theologies growing out of the fourth step, which discovered and refined the logical power of language to understand and anticipate the world of experience, the full power of modern science for vastly increasing man's expansion of knowledge did not emerge until a few centuries ago. The secret of the new sciences, from the time of Copernicus and Galileo, was the discovery that neither the traditional nor intuited premises, implicit or explicit, in a symbolic model of the real world are necessarily true. They are at best rough approximations, and there needs to be, first, some way of testing their validity and, second, some way of inventing a cleaner, purer formulation of the conceptual or symbolic system so that it may better accord with the facts of experience.

The first of these needs is the system of empirical testing. This means careful observation of what actually happens and noting how well it conforms to the linguistic or other symbolic model or theory. The second of these needs is illustrated by what happened to the Greek or Ptolemaic model of the solar system, which worked very well within the limits of astronomical observation for a long time. But by the time of Copernicus the empirical observations required more and more minor repairs in order to get a good correlation between the theoretical model and the actual events observed. Copernicus imagined (thanks to the brain's capacity to project variant patterns of symbols for summing up the contents of its memory bank of experience) a different model, with the sun instead of the earth as a center for heavenly motions. This is a sort of artistic invention, a new perspective, a new frame of reference, a novel hypothesis about some imaginary, not directly observable machinery or model of the way things are, which then is found to fit the observed facts better.

In summary I should like to emphasize that in each of these five successive ways in which man has come to know right from wrong there is a common feature. At each level in the process of establishing patterns of right behavior, from the variety of relatively random behaviors a few and only a few are selected because they are right and viable. B. F. Skinner brought this to our attention here on Star Island about ten years ago when he told us about the "operant reinforcement"—a "natural selection" of more or less random behavioral responses. Present notions of evolution and development suggest that this process is going on in the "natural selection" of randomly produced inputs into molecular aggregations, of randomly produced inputs or mutations of genotypes, of randomly produced inputs into bisexual recombinations of genetic patterns, of randomly produced inputs of environmental factors impinging on the surface of a living cell, of randomly produced inputs into the patterns in a central nervous system or brain, of randomly produced inputs into the behavioral patterns in primitive cultures, of randomly produced inputs into the logical computers possessed by brains informed or structured by culturally transmitted languages, and of randomly produced inputs (from the scanning of memory banks and sensory inputs) into the structured forebrain of an artist or scientist. This recurrent theme of random trials followed by selection, which I ascribe to all levels of emergence of stable and viable patterns of life, is perhaps not a very clearly documented or accepted scientific generalization, at least not in the sweeping form in which I have presented it. Nevertheless it is to me a very reasonable one, and one that has tremendous value for a theology grounded in the sciences, for it reveals a common generator and determiner of human and all destiny. (Subsequent to the preparation of this paper, B. F. Skinner has published a paper which shows beautifully the essential functional identity between "natural selection" in the long-term learning of organic species and the "operant conditioning or reinforcement" of short-term learning that goes on as an organism develops from birth to death. This reinforces my generalization by thus linking these two major categories of "learning."[31])

Science and Knowledge of Good and Evil

Today, scientists generally recognize that there is no perfect and final knowledge in the possession of man, and that ultimate truth in a finite knower is an impossibility. What they assert instead is that there are no limits to man's improving his models, his images, his language about the world of reality. For scientists there is the possibility of ever more adequate truth, even if not ultimate truth.

I do not need to labor the fact that the scientific way of learning new truth is the fastest and most effective yet evolved. On this account we can say it is the highest of the five steps of learning or knowing that I have named. It has been doubling the amount of our information in something like every ten or fifteen years. If it keeps on at this rate, in another century we may know one hundred to one thousand times as much as we know now.

I perhaps do need to labor a bit the fact that the scientific kind of increase in knowledge can and must apply to our knowledge of morals, of right and wrong, of good and evil.

As I indicated at the beginning, science suggests that, for living systems, life is the supreme or intrinsic value for which all other values are instrumental. That life and the instrumental values productive of life are established as values by the cosmos is implicit in the extension of the hypothesis of natural selection back to chemical evolution. The reasonable hypothesis is that the cosmos produced life on earth, and probably on many other earths in a cosmos of billions of galaxies. We have heard Shapley tell this story here: the evolution of life is a natural product of the way things are in the cosmos, from hydrogen and the laws of its behavior.[32] And for each living species, from the most primitive, the value of life is established in its genotype by the selective forces of the physics and chemistry of the molecules of the genotype operating in the physics or chemistry of the local environment provided by the cosmos, including, of course, the physics of the other molecules of the cell, the neighboring cells, and the environing milieu, inanimate and animate.

All species, which have by some error valued something else more than what this nature requires for their continuation, simply have not continued in being. In terms of recent scientific views of life, it is almost tautological to say that if any of these metastable systems of order, living in a disordering environment, fail to integrate all their parts and behaviors to support the maintenance of this order, then they are automatically swallowed up by the surrounding disordering, entropic world, and become void and without form or life. The moment you do not prefer life to death, you die. Here, of course, I am not referring to superficial and sometimes misleading verbal expressions of preference but to the organized activity of the many billions of cells that constitute a living man, even though he inanely declares he prefers death to life. Nor do I refer merely to the life of those billions of cells that constitute the temporary bodily or organic expression of a combined genetic and cultural code of life; for Wald and others here have made clear to us that the higher living systems require the death of the body in order that the genotype may grow to new and higher levels. This germ plasm or genotype is a sort of inner soul of organic life that does not necessarily die as the body or organism does; but in man and other living species it has been in continuous existence and growth for billions of years.

I repeat the fact that most religions have recognized life as the supreme value or good, not excepting the Judaeo-Christian tradition. One of the great commands of the Lord to man in the biblical Genesis is to choose life rather than death. I call your attention also to a religious sect, the Shakers, which held that mortal life for descendants was not sacred, that marriage, sexual intercourse, and children were wrong rather than right. All that remains of any such religion, after one generation of faithful followers passes away, are "fossils" to remind us that they are no more. I once lived in a town where there remained the empty farmhouses and barns of these Shakers whose rules of right and wrong were wrong. I do not mean to say that the dinosaurs and Shakers did not in some way contribute to and perhaps enhance our life. I mean simply that they did not embody the ultimate value of living systems: life. There is only one judge of what is sacred for living beings and that is survival, according to both the scientific and most religious pictures.

Science does more than tell us what is our most sacred value, it tells us how to recognize as yet undiscovered elements of the instrumental value hierarchy, which reaches its apex in maintaining and increasing life's order, much more acutely than was possible by earlier religions and philosophies. Schrödinger's notion that life is a process that feeds on the entropic or decaying-order process is a definition of the nature of life that will surely prove to be a guide to our intellectual quest for understanding and evaluating the hierarchy of our values. Once there is opened to man the insight that life is his supreme value and that it is defined in the basic laws and events of the universe, then he has indefinite facilities for approaching human values through the sciences.

One of the interesting sidelights provided by this scientific picture of man and his values is that a value is essentially the same thing as information or knowledge. Schrödinger[33] and Wiener[34] both pointed out that this anti-entropic evolutionary direction of life or increasing order was mathematically identical with what we call information. It is common today to speak, as Hoagland did, of the information cumulated in the gene pool as defining life. This accumulation of information, from our most primitive ancestors of many million years ago to the present moment, is the incarnation of the basic values of our system of life. Now the dominantly unself-conscious nature of this information should not cause misunderstanding. This scientific use of "information" does not require that information be self-conscious. The higher nervous systems of the most evolved animals and man, which provide a limited self-consciousness, are simply a special case of a general program of increasing information. Consciousness is an emergent phenomenon, as is life itself, in this long evolutionary history of new and better ways to accumulate information or life.

Knowledge of Good versus Good Behavior

I have suggested that the sciences have emerged as the latest and best way of accumulating information and that information is negentropic like life and the cardinal defining value of life. I, and others at this conference, have shown something of how the sciences reveal or make conscious the values and the value-producing mechanisms of preconscious life. But we have had questions that still bother many of us. Granted that we can have knowledge about values, does this help us in behaving according to these values? St. Paul was not the first or the last to complain that he did that which he knew he should not do and did not do that which he knew he should. It has been

suggested that religion is not a matter of knowledge or understanding or information but of feeling. The ethically minded
might suggest it is not even sufficient to say religion is feeling: it
must be right or moral behavior or deeds. What do I think the
sciences can answer to this problem?

First, let it be noted that in the accumulation of information
or wisdom about life in the genotype one cannot separate the
information from behavior. The ten billion commandments in
the genotype are ordinarily executed to the letter of the law, or
wisdom for living thus laid down, to every last jot and tittle.
The love and mutual concern often sacrificial of life, of the
members of the ant colony, who devote themselves, their lives
to the various chores of mutual support and duty in the
community, are genotypically informed, and values thus
informed are so enacted. One could properly say that moral
behavior and moral information for ants are the same thing, if
one is willing to allow the terms "moral" and "information" to
apply to the underlying unconscious mechanisms. And the
problem that St. Paul complained of does not exist at this level.

The problem of the distinction between information and
behavior is introduced at the level of the central nervous
system, as Riddle has told us. The problem is that of having to
make choices in situations where it is not always immediately
clear which choice is higher in the hierarchy of values impressed upon the brain by the genotype in combination with its
learning experience in a human culture. Hoagland and Ward
Goodenough have made it clear that in human beings there are
hierarchies of values. It is the function of the brain or central
nervous system to seek, in the midst of the tremendous amount
of complex information and complex value hierarchies present
in the patterns of the nervous tissue, the optimum path, the
path of most significant value for life. As Wallace told us in
1961, this brain and the religious systems it harbors seek to
maximize the good or life and minimize the threats thereto.[35]

The seeming conflict of values between one particular conscious desire or intent and a different direction in the actual
behavior is the result of the fact that we are not conscious of
most of the tremendously difficult and complex operations by
which we make the choices of optimum value. We are not
conscious of all the information involved in the decision pro-

cess that leads to our actions. The religious problem of evil is revealed in new clarity by this scientific picture of the problems of getting a right answer by means of this machinery we call the brain.

Although the genotypic "moral code," the genotypic code for good behavior, is always followed to the letter of the law, the law in the genotype is not perfect. It is full of errors. As Hoagland pointed out, about a third of all biological conceptions are not viable. In the genotypic codes, as in human social codes of right and wrong, there is no perfect code. We have heard much about "moral relativism" at this conference. It begins in the genetic stage, and it continues in the stage of the central nervous system, because the input from both genotype and culture contains error. Living systems simply are not fully preadapted to all future contingencies. It would seem that we can epitomize the program of life as the unending search for the right code without our ever fully reaching it. This is parallel to our earlier note that scientific knowledge may ever improve without reaching any ultimate or absolute truth. If the failures and inadequacies of the codes of right behavior of any time and place are always with us, to that extent we are always wrong, bad, and evil. And since in evolutionary pictures of life this is the case, we may say that man in this sense is inherently wrong, bad, and evil. One finds this parallel to religious doctrines of original sin.

However, it should be noted that this same process in another perspective is good. If life is the supreme value, it is clear that in this universe it can be obtained only by this unending program of trial and error, which continues to build up higher and higher systems of order or life. In this wider perspective evil becomes the agent of the good, wrong or error the means to the right, and death the source of greater life.[36] Hence the sciences may here be providing the basis for a resolution of an ancient religious paradox.

The third and fourth steps of collecting information, including sacred and moral information, were cultural. The third was accumulation of wisdom, which our ancestors came across largely by accident but which, when it provided better adaptation to the conditions of life, was selected to be remembered and transmitted by the symbolic systems of behavior, including language. The fourth step was the more conscious utilization of the logical powers of language.

The transmission systems for these two ways of cultural accumulation of moral wisdom were, by their nature, pretty closely tied to the pain and pleasure mechanisms of the brain. The social conditioning or educating process had been largely successful in tying or conditioning socially transmitted duties, hopes, and fears to the basic motivational system as these were internalized in the brain or, as some might say, in the conscience or in the superego.[37]

Moreover, the cultural rules for right and wrong seldom conflicted greatly with the less sacred or less moral input of the culture into the brain. As Ward Goodenough pointed out, the transition from the hunting and gathering stages of life to the agricultural and then to the early urban were accompanied by corresponding changes in the patterns and methods of enforcing right and wrong behavior.

Disintegration of Value Structures of Higher Cultural Levels Means Death

But since the rise of the extremely rapid methods of gaining new knowledge and creating entirely new circumstances of life, which began with the modern sciences a few centuries ago, there has not been a correspondingly rapid evolution in our value structures and the sanctions thereof. This lag of the moral and religious aspects of culture relative to the general explosion of knowledge and the corresponding explosion of technology, with its radical alterations of the conditions of life, leaves mankind in its most vulnerable condition in perhaps millions of years. Hoagland has pointed this up in the context of the atom bomb, and Ward Goodenough in terms of the conflict of cultures in a suddenly small world which technology has produced.

We are all aware of the fact that the old religious beliefs have evaporated, leaving us with rather feeble religious sanctions for morality. I, and increasing millions of others, cannot accept the revelations of the fourth step of knowledge where they conflict with those of the fifth step. There are many here and elsewhere who have questioned the adequacy of secular sanctions, by government, law, police, or armies. Many have wondered whether there are any objective sanctions or criteria for the validity of any of the plurality of ethical systems of right and wrong.

Relativism or subjective morality carried to the extreme is a defeat of the whole idea of a social code of right and wrong that Ward Goodenough has said is essential for social life; and he is backed by considerable social-science opinion in this.[38] Many who have left the churches of the West suppose that there is no problem. Their assumption is often like that of some of the religious liberals who suppose that man is somehow natively endowed with adequate values, and by this they can hardly mean anything other than that the genotype alone, apart from religious beliefs, is a sufficient basis for goodness.

But I think the cultural anthropologists and some other social scientists are backing the convictions of more conservative leaders of religion: that a human society cannot long endure in a state of anomie, in the absence of a more or less coherent culturally transmitted norm or hierarchical system of values. The genotypically transmitted hierarchy of values was not sufficient even for primitive human cultures. Already then, religious systems provided the cultural supplementations of genetic values necessary to their particular societies. As Ward Goodenough pointed out, the different cultural and religious traditions are variant adaptations, representing different cultural species. They are no more identical or alike than the different species of fish are; but like the fish adaptations they all have to meet certain common problems, such as sex, death, property rights, etc., and each culture or religion represents a viable adaptation under the particular circumstances of the time and place where it has flourished. The cultural anthropologists and sociologists and psychologists have found that, when the central value beliefs represented in religions of a primitive or advanced society begin to break up, the people at the same time experience an increase in mental and social breakdown until there is a religious revitalization or a conversion to a more adequate religious and moral system.[39]

If it be true, as is suggested by many analysts, that the cultures of the various higher religious traditions of the world today are dissolving in the face of the new information revealed by the sciences, and if it also be true that genotypic wisdom is

by itself insufficient to generate adequate motivation or structure for human social life in an age of science, where shall we
find our authority for values?

I conclude by saying that the sciences as sources of valid
information and new revelations are our best hope. They
contain the most complete and validated information about the
nature of man and about the nature of the realities that created
him, sustain him, and determine his destiny. The sciences led
me to discard the still widespread twentieth-century supposition that it is not possible to have objective truth about values,
about either the cultural moral codes of right and wrong or the
organic values produced in the genotype. I have been greatly
impressed by the finding of the evolutionary theory of adaptation that there is an external reality with which all creatures
must come to terms, an objective reality that imposes our
values upon us. In my opinion such a non-human source of
values, a superhuman source in that it determines what men
shall do rather than vice versa, is equivalent to what the
religions have called a god, a god that is now revealed by the
sciences as the system of reality upon which our lives are
dependent, a reality that is involved in judging by selection, not
only our genetic wisdom, but our cultural wisdom. The present
scientific picture as I read it says that all life, including human
psychological and cultural patterns, is selected by a single
system of reality that operates eternally to define what is good
or evil for all patterns of life. Today the sciences are our best
sources of revelation as to its nature and its requirements for
either genetic or cultural adaptation, and hence for the necessary revisions of our knowledge of right and wrong.

Furthermore, information, whether in the genotype, the
primitive brain, primitive religion, rational religion, or the
sciences, is tied hand and glove with human feelings and
behavior; and we therefore need not fear what many mistakenly believe: that such information is unable to influence
our deepest emotions and behavior.

As I said in the beginning, I do not intend to present specific
codes of right and wrong or good and evil, only a generalized
picture as to where we have gotten them in the past and where
I think we are going to get them in the future. I have been
asking only: how do and how can we know right from wrong?

NOTES

1. (*a*) Sol Tax (ed.), *Evolution after Darwin* (3 vols.; Chicago: University of Chicago Press, 1960). These volumes contain papers ranging in topic from cosmic and chemical evolution through biological to cultural evolution. (*b*) Anne Roe and George Gaylord Simpson (eds.), *Behavior and Evolution* (New Haven, Conn.: Yale University Press, 1958). (*c*) John R. Platt (ed.), *New Views of the Nature of Man* (Chicago: University of Chicago Press, 1965). (*d*) Harlow Shapley (ed.), *Science Ponders Religion* (New York: Appleton-Century-Crofts, 1960). (*e*) Hudson Hoagland and Ralph W. Burhoe (eds.), *Evolution and Man's Progress* (New York: Columbia University Press, 1962). (*f*) Theodosius Dobzhansky, *Mankind Evolving* (New Haven, Conn.: Yale University Press, 1962). (*g*) Bentley Glass, *Science and Ethical Values* (Chapel Hill: University of North Carolina Press, 1965). (*h*) D. O. Hebb, *Organization of Behavior* (New York: John Wiley & Sons, 1949). (*i*) M. F. Ashley Montagu, *The Direction of Human Development* (New York: Harper & Row, 1955). (*j*) C. H. Waddington, *The Ethical Animal* (New York: Atheneum Publishers, 1961).

2. Cf., e.g., George Wald's statement in *Zygon*, I, No. 1 (March, 1966), 46.

3. Cf., A. I. Oparin, *The Origin of Life* (New York: Macmillan Co., 1938; 2nd ed., Dover Publications, 1953). Molecular evolution leading to life and the pioneering work of Oparin were first brought to the attention of this conference in 1954, when George Wald gave a version of a paper, "The Origin of Life," which was published in the *Scientific American* of August, 1954. In the decade following that paper, remarkable progress has been made in clarifying our understanding of the physical forces molding the evolution of molecular structures into living systems and molding the subsequent evolution of life. This will be found reflected in Wald's "The Origins of Life" published in the *Proceedings of the National Academy of Sciences* for August, 1964.

4. Erwin Schrödinger, *What Is Life?* (New York: Doubleday & Co., 1956).

5. Norbert Wiener, *The Human Use of Human Beings* (Boston: Houghton Mifflin, 1950; paperback, New York: Doubleday & Co., 1954).

6. Schrödinger, *op. cit.* (n. 4), p. 75.

7. Oparin, *op. cit.* (n. 3), p. 192; also Hans Gaffron, "The Origin of Life," in Tax (ed.), *op. cit.* (n. 1*a*), I, 40. I might point out that this broad conception of "natural selection" as the inherent character or law, being revealed by the sciences, of the way things happen in this cosmos, provides for me a rational and consoling attitude toward some of the perplexing problems of man's future. No matter what wild cultural schemes we may devise, no matter even if we establish cybernetic machines that can exceed all that human societies now can perform, no matter what competing patterns of life may be found elsewhere in the cosmos, we can hypothesize or have faith that, so long as variant or competing trials keep the program open, natural selection will continue to select ever more stable and higher patterns of order or life. We have here the grounds for a scientifically credible concept of a god, or

ultimate ground of life, determining all destiny (and hence good), including man's. I am developing such a cosmic theology in other papers.

8. See, e.g., Wiener, *op. cit.* (n. 5), p. 40.

9. Anthony F. C. Wallace, *Religion: An Anthropological View* (New York: Random House, 1966), p. 38.

10. See, e.g., Hudson Hoagland's "Ethology and Ethics—The Biology of Right and Wrong" *Zygon* 2, No. 1 (1967): 77-96, which was also given at this 1965 IRAS conference, and his "The Brain and Crises in Human Values," *Zygon*, I, No. 2 (June, 1966), 140-57.

11. Harlow Shapley, "Life, Hope, and Cosmic Evolution," *Zygon*, I, No. 3 (September, 1966), 275-85.

12. Oscar Riddle, "The Emergence of Good and Evil," *Zygon* 2, No. 1 (1967): 34-42.

13. Walter B. Cannon, *The Wisdom of the Body* (New York: W. W. Norton & Co., 1932).

14. Th. Dobzhansky, "Mankind Consorting with Things Eternal," in Shapley (ed.), *op. cit.* (n. 1*d*), pp. 117-35.

15. A. E. Emerson, "Dynamic Homeostasis: A Unifying Principle in Organic, Social, and Ethical Evolution," *Scientific Monthly,* LXXVIII, No. 2 (February, 1954), 67-85; his "Human Cultural Evolution and Its Relation to Organic Evolution of Termites," *Termites in the Humid Tropics, Proceedings of the New Delhi Symposium* (Humid Tropics Research) (Paris: UNESCO, 1962); or the briefer treatment on pp. 319-21 of his paper "The Evolution of Adaptation in Population Systems," in Tax (ed.), *op. cit.* (n. 1*a*), I, 307-48.

16. R. W. Gerard, "Comments on Religion in an Age of Science," in Shapley (ed.), *op. cit.* (n. 1*d*), p. 89.

17. Hudson Hoagland, "Some Reflections on Science and Religion," in Shapley (ed.), *op. cit.* (n. 1*d*), p. 27.

18. A. G. Huntsman, "Poised between the Dictates of Nature and a Peculiar Freedom," in Shapley (ed.), *op. cit.* (n. 1*d*), p. 191.

19. A. Montagu (see n. 1*i*).

20. H. A. Murray, "Two Versions of Man," in Shapley (ed.), *op. cit.* (n. 1*d*), p. 159.

21. Wald, *loc. cit.* (n. 2).

22. Emerson, "Human Cultural Evolution and Its Relation to Organic Evolution of Termites" (n. 15), pp. 2-3.

23. R. S. Morison, "Darwinism: Foundation for an Ethical System?" *Zygon,* I, No. 4 (December, 1966), 348.

24. W. Goodenough, "Human Purpose in Life," *Zygon,* I, No. 3 (September, 1966): 218; and also his "Right and Wrong in Human Evolution," *Zygon* 2, No. 1 (1967): 59-76.

25. Hoagland, *op. cit.* (n. 10).

26. Dobzhansky, "Mankind Consorting with Things Eternal" (n. 14), p. 128.

27. Emerson, "Dynamic Homeostasis . . ." (n. 15), p. 70.

28. See the following notes: 1*a, b, e, f, g, i, j:* 10: 15: 24: see also Julian S. Huxley, "Evolution, Cultural and Biological," in W. Thomas (ed.), *Yearbook of Anthropology* (New York: Wenner-Gren Foundation for Anthropological

Research, 1955); Clifford Geertz, "The Impact of the Concept of Culture on the Concept of Man," in Platt (ed.), *op. cit.* (n. 1c), pp. 93-118; Clyde Kluckhohn, "The Scientific Study of Values and Contemporary Civilization," *Zygon*, I, No. 3 (September, 1966), 230-43; Robert S. Morison, "Where is Biology Taking Us?" *Science,* CLV (January 27, 1967), 429-33; this and the paper by Th. Dobzhansky, "Changing Man," *Science,* CLV (January 27, 1967), 409-15, are stimulating papers on this theme that come to my attention as this issue of *Zygon* goes to press; B. F. Skinner, "The Phylogeny and Ontogeny of Behavior," *Science,* CLIII (September 9, 1966), pp 1205-13.

29. Emerson, "Dynamic Homeostasis . . ."(n. 15), p. 71.

30. William Ernest Hocking, *The Coming World Civilization* (New York: Harper & Row, 1956), p. 17.

31. Skinner, *op. cit.* (n. 28). This paper also reinforces my next point, about the lack of perfection inherent in man, at the level of behavioral ontogeny or development. The impossibility of perfection at the genetic and phylogenetic level has been clearly made by the geneticists and evolutionary theorists.

32. Harlow Shapley, *Of Stars and Men* (Boston: Beacon Press, 1958).

33. Schrödinger, *op. cit.* (n. 4).

34. Wiener, *op. cit.* (n. 5), pp. 21, 32.

35. Wallace, *op. cit.* (n. 9), p. 38.

36. See, e.g., the following papers in *Zygon*, I, No. 4 (December, 1966): Theodosius Dobzhansky, "An Essay on Religion, Death, and Evolutionary Adaptation," pp. 317-31; Morison, "Darwinism: Foundation for an Ethical System?" pp. 347-53; J. P.Warbasse, "On Life and Death and Immortality," pp. 366-72.

37. B. F. Skinner, "The Design of Cultures," in Hoagland and Burhoe (eds.), *op. cit.* (n. 1e), pp. 124-36; Emerson, "Dynamic Homeostasis . . ." (n. 15), p. 67; see also n. 10.

38. See, e.g., the following papers in *Zygon:* Anthony F. C. Wallace, "Rituals: Sacred and Profane," I, No. 1 (March, 1966), 60-81; L. K. Frank, "Man's Changing Image of Himself," I, No. 2 (June, 1966), 158-80; and Kluckhohn, *op. cit.* (n. 28).

39. See Wallace, *Religion: An Anthropological View* (n. 9); Murray, *op. cit.* (n. 20); and Skinner, "The Phylogeny and Ontogeny of Behavior" (n. 28).

4

*Natural Selection and God**

One of the prime elements of a scientifically grounded theology is the rebirth or renewal of credibility in an objective reality that determines destiny. Religious belief systems characteristically involve man's relation or adaptation to some ultimate realities which vastly transcend man's power and whose laws man must discover and obey if he is to be saved, that is, if he is to have a good life or even any life. Such realities are known as gods, or in the higher religions as the one God or the one ultimate reality. I wish to point out how closely contemporary scientific belief systems portray man's relation to a similarly all-encompassing and all-controlling reality and to examine the relevance of this scientific portrayal for religious belief in an age of science.

In scientific discussions there is little doubt about the function of what Darwin called "natural selection" in determining or shaping the evolution or destiny of organic species. Human genetic heritage, or man's genotype, is increasingly understood to have been established and continually maintained by natural selection. In this essay, I wish to examine some of the parallels between the religious concepts of, or characteristics ascribed to, God and the scientific concepts of, or characteristics ascribed to, nature and natural selection. If what appears to me to be the case is further substantiated, it may be that instead of

*This chapter is a revision of part of a paper prepared for a seminar on April 17, 1970, of the Center for Advanced Study in Theology and the Sciences of the Meadville/Lombard Theological School. It was first published in *Zygon* 7(1): 30–63, March 1972.

a dead God killed by modern knowledge, as Nietzsche suggested, we may shortly come to see that we have a very live
God, revealed (unveiled) by the sciences mostly since the time
Nietzsche wrote. Moreover, I suggest that this God will be
found to possess many of the same prime characteristics as the
divinity of the higher religions and will become the focus of
man's concern, the guide of his moral behavior, and the
comfort of his soul—in short, the center of the rebirth of a
religion adapted to universal viability among all people in a
coming age of science and scientific technology in which man's
civilization will rise to heights scarcely yet dreamed of by most
men alive today.

But in the Judaeo-Christian culture of the West there are
two big obstacles to understanding scientific accounts of
natural selection as descriptive of God, that is, to understanding natural selection as the ultimate and fascinating power to
which man may ascribe the marvels and wonder of the creation
and continued ordering of all things, including man's own
privileged powers as the most advanced creature on earth and
as a subordinate cocreator; and to recognizing natural selection
as the ultimate and awful judge whose laws man must find and
obey if he is to continue thus to flourish.

The first obstacle is the widespread misconception which
supposes there is a dualistic character of the world of human
experience, or a separation between man's spirit or mind on
the one hand and the natural, physical, bodily world on the
other. This dualism stems in the West more from the impact of
Greek ways of viewing things a couple of thousand years ago
than from the Judaic views. It is a prevalent or reigning view
today not only among theologians but also among the scholars
and practitioners (poets, artists, etc.) of the humanities in
general, and saturates the literature and general culture that
permeates the West. A similar dualistic misconception may
inhibit a scientific doctrine of man in Eastern culture.

The important point is that, wherever it occurs, the belief
that the universe (and man, too) is composed of two separate
natures, causes a logical chasm that disrupts making rational
conclusions from material and scientific facts so that they apply
to the other realm of human experience, which is the realm
man naturally holds to be the significant one—the spiritual,

mental, aesthetic, and volitional aspects of the universe, the gods, or men. The objection to this dualism is not with its assertion of the reality and importance for man of his feelings, wishes, desires, etc., but with the impotence of the dualistic system today to provide credible conclusions about consequences for human feelings by means of any statements that involve the natural, objective world. If the human mind, spirit, and feelings are presumed to be even only partly free from and independent of the natural world, this logical chasm confuses and frustrates any compelling and clear conclusions of any arguments that move from one of these separated domains to the other.

As a result, evidences from nature about God or mortality tend to become ineffective. In a scientific world, this means the death of credibility in God. But the big obstacle to understanding the role of such a superhuman, objective reality or God as being played by "nature"—that is, by the scientifically described cosmic scheme in creating and supervising man's continuing development—is the as yet poorly understood role of natural factors beyond man's control in the selection or shaping of human personal and social life.

The second obstacle is the aversion, even by some scientists, to the role of "natural selection" in human personal and social affairs. This aversion stems in part from the same dualistic belief and also from a corrective reaction to an unwarranted spread of the somewhat badly conceived and unsubstantiated doctrines of social Darwinism in the late nineteenth century. During the succeeding half-century blackout on speculation about the processes of cultural evolution, only a handful of anthropologists have tried to form theories about it, and these did not gain widespread favor. The Marxist doctrines were perhaps discounted as being more political than scientific, and to the minds of sophisticated anthropologists, either the evolutionary theories of culture seemed to be too simplified to account for the subtle variety of observed facts about human culture or else data gathering seemed more important than theorizing.[1]

In psychology, there was also only a slim few who continued to feel that natural selection was important for human psychology, but often these were the ones who made the mistake of supposing that human behavior was, like animal behavior, fully programmed in the genetic heritage, who failed to understand the very real and important structuring of human behavior by external, nongenetic heritages, and who hence tended to be rejected.

By the middle of the twentieth century, with some stimulation from some geneticists like Theodosius Dobzhansky,[2] from some biological theoreticians of evolution like Julian Huxley, and from psychologists like B. F. Skinner, a new development in scientific circles about the nature of cultural heritage and its evolution began to take place. I find particularly significant, scientifically and theologically, the notion that the memory of partially random or accidental discoveries of men is transmitted (communicated and imitated or replicated) in the behavioral patterns of men, after being selected for their experienced or imagined usefulness. The psychological dynamics of this is illumined by the writings of B. F. Skinner suggesting that conditioning or reinforcement of behavior patterns was essentially a kind of natural-selection process in personal or individual development (ontogeny).[3]

But this new approach has just gotten under way, and the major part of both scientific and humanistic communities still shun a naturalistic doctrine of man. A complete analysis of the failure to find natural-selection doctrines for accounting for human behavior is much more complex than this, but I shall only mention four other factors contributing to this failure.

1. The data gathering of the anthropologists contributed to the fact that there is a wide range of variable cultural patterns. From this fact developed the notion of "cultural relativity," the notion that different moral or value patterns existed in quite viable societies. From this, many commentators drew the false conclusion that patterns of human life could be anything anyone wanted. This tended to diminish the effectiveness of the notions of any natural necessities applying to human cultural and behavioral patterns.

2. The same tendency to diminish faith in any compulsions on man from nature was propagated by the understandable concern of social philosophers in recent centuries with the problem of "human freedom," and some interpreters of this borrowed erroneously from the early twentieth-century pro-

nouncements concerning the Heisenberg principle of indeterminacy or uncertainty in physics. This was commonly interpreted to mean that if, even in physics (the heretofore most rigorously deterministic picture of the world), there was in the end no real determinism, then certainly there was no compulsion or necessity placed by nature upon man.

3. The notion of "natural selection" among geneticists has itself been stripped of its nineteenth-century connotation of explanation of survival by natural forces, and it has become more of a statistical or descriptive term referring technically only to the fact that certain genetic patterns are found to have more offspring than others. The attempt to theorize or demonstrate an explanation of how "fitness" or "adaptation" is worked out in terms of greater efficiencies of one or another kind of mechanism seems to play a lesser role than the definition of "fitness" as simply a measure of the "number of offspring."[4] While important for the development of evolutionary theory in terms of genotypic statistics, this trend has tended to mask analysis of the detailed mechanics of why the natural circumstances of the interacting elements result in the survival (in greater numbers or over longer time) of one species or genetic population than another.[5]

4. Lastly, during the past couple of centuries, the freedom of the scientific community to seek after its doctrines of "natural determinism" was won by a tacit truce with the humanities, still the dominant regime of the educational community in most places even today, whereby scientists kept hands off any attempts to explain human psychology and society in terms of natural law.[6] The psychosocial "sciences" are only about a century old, they have been frightening to many in their deterministic expressions, such as Marxist social doctrine or Pavlovian and behavioral psychology, and their status as sciences is fought by partisans from both the humanistic and the scientific wings of our dualistic culture.[7] There has been a tendency to say "social studies" rather than "social sciences."

But, in any case, neither the humanistic philosophers nor the theologians have very often favored any doctrines that imply a natural selection or determination of the nature and behavior of man.

Natural Selection and the Death of God

Here we should look a little more closely at what the term "natural selection" does and can mean. Darwin used it to distinguish it from human selection used by agricultural breeders. It was also a term intended to assert that it was not so much a superanthropoid god who fabricated life as it was "nature": the natural world surrounding, or the environment of, living organisms. Strictly speaking, the nature that does the selecting includes not only the surrounding world but also the nature in the very guts of the living system itself, including the nature of the very molecules that make up the sub-units and genetic memory of each cell. If one traces the history of evolving life back in time long enough, one comes to a point where the surrounding nonliving world is all there is, for no life has yet arisen. Hence, sooner or later in scientific explanation, the nonliving or physical nature of the world becomes the creator, guide, judge, and sustainer of life. Living systems are a special class of phenomena of the physical world. "Natural selection" is another way of saying "the naturally stable configurations reached by open systems of the matter of the universe through random trial-and-error motions." This is equivalent to "survival of the fittest," or, from the genetic perspective, "progeny (descendants or replications) that continue to exist in large numbers or, better, for a long time in the future."

Stable systems are systems that are not easily broken up by the randomizing energies in the habitat or environment which they inhabit. *Open* systems are defined by boundaries, like the skin of an organism, through which materials and energy may pass. A *living system* is a *stable, open* system which so selects the inflow and outflow of matter and energy and so regulates the behavior inside the bounding skin that the characteristic patterns of organization are maintained in spite of the randomizing energies and materials impinging on the system. The *skin* may range from the molecular film covering a cell to the biosphere representing the boundary of living species that form a mantle on the earth's surface.

The recent scientific views of the prehuman and preanimate nature of the world as the creator and selector or judge of what shall live would, of course, be a denial of a god who operated anthropomorphically (that is, who worked and planned and designed the way men do). Hence, natural selection would seem to be a denial of divine creation by a manlike god. However, it should be noted that, from the view of god meaning the ultimate constellation of forces outside of and prior to life (including man) that did in fact create and sustain life, nature or natural selection is in reality a modern statement or revelation of such a god's nature. Darwin was accused of renaming God. The process of natural selection, indeed, may be said to be a reformation of the doctrine of god, although the "nonhuman" character of this concept of the creator of man led theologians to reject it as what they and their predecessors meant by god.[8] But, it is this doctrine of elements intrinsic to nature as the source, creator, and judge of man which has been growing in the scientific and public mind in the century since Darwin. Since it is a widely accepted doctrine in the scientific community, theologians today, if they want to portray a living god rather than a dead god, ought seriously to consider integrating it into their systems of concepts.

As I have indicated above, one of the reasons this new revelation of the nature of the source and judge of our being is not adopted in the theological community is the fact that it has not yet been clearly visualized or adopted in the psychosocial sciences. However, even the theologians, at least many of the sophisticated ones, have within the century after Darwin pretty well accepted the doctrine of natural selection for organic evolution as "true" for science and public education, even though most of them seem to retain the conception that man's "spirit" is in a separate world. For a half-century, the liberal theologians have widely accepted this doctrine of natural selection to account for man's body, and even a century ago some daring liberal theologians (e.g., Francis Ellingwood Abbot)[9] had already accepted Darwin's picture of man's creation and evolution and had started to build a reformed theology in this light. In the 1970s it is only among the uneducated where the cultural lag permits serious doubt of organic evolution by natural selection. Of course, there are millions of people in the United States and in other parts of the world where modern evolutionary theory is not acceptable in public schools or in general conversation. There is still some organized resistance

to it.[10] But such backwaters of the old cultural riverbed, even
when they are sizable, do not represent the trend of the future,
when popular magazines like *Life* and when television shows
present vivid pictures of recent evolutionary theory. Hence,
neither these backwaters nor the clergy can be held to be
serious stumbling blocks to theological acceptance that scientific doctrines of organic evolution are "true."

Western social philosophy, and the historical and some areas
of psychosocial scholarship, may be more responsible than
theology for our culture's shunning a doctrine of man's cultural
and individual development as determined by some lawful
selective process. Many have argued that man is free to make
his own history and culture as he likes. Implicit in their image
of man is the dualistic notion that the significant part of man's
nature is independent of natural law, or determination or
selection by nature. Many mistakenly used the implications of
man's success in technological inventions to imply that he was
master over nature rather than subject to natural laws. They
were obviously unaware that technological increase in the
amount of food or power comes *not* from a superior power in
man's voluntarism or willing, but rather from man's better
understanding of nature's laws and adaptation to what nature
requires.

Theologians tended to find the dualistic view more congenial
and not to see in nature or nature's laws their favored notions
of God or man. It was natural, therefore, especially among
"liberal" Christian theologians who were concerned with
man's voluntaristic or "free" behavior to help himself and his
fellowmen out of their miseries, that there would be a trend
away from predestination by an almighty God toward the
doctrines of man's independence from superhuman or objective laws. They found support for their convictions in the
reigning interpretations of man derivable from some of the
humanistic exponents of historical and psychosocial studies
whose dualistic views of man also derived from the classical
Greek philosophy that had become a part of Christian theology's frame. These doctrines found man transcendent over his
natural environment and free to do many wonderful things of
his own volition, independently of his environment, a view
which is valid if explanation is not examined too deeply.

Hence, if man had only his fellowmen to fear, since his scientifically based technology seemed largely to free him from fear of nonhuman nature, it would seem clear that theology and religious practice should turn more and more toward a moral or ethical exhortation of some presupposed human values that thus could be evoked.

One interpretation of recent religious history could be that, although the old superman god or godman was still invoked as father and sponsor of the moral program, the public had decreasing faith that this god made any difference. It was doubtful that there was much reality in, or much room for, significant and meaningful operations by a god which, the theologians as well as other scholars had declared, was dissociated from the realm of the laws that do in fact rule nature, dissociated from the world the sciences reveal and a world in which most people sooner or later come to believe, often simply because of the success of technology. Moreover, whether or not God operates through physical nature, God's operations could hardly have any effect on a man who, as some theologians have implied, was in any case free to choose and make himself and his world what he willed, a man free from ultimate dominance or control by any outside realities. A philosophy that asserts existing human values are supreme and that man is not bound by some outside reality leaves man in charge of his own fate. It tends toward a doctrine of the sufficiency of man unto himself. It results in the declaration that "God is dead" or "God is absent."

Insofar as "God" is a term that means some superior, objective reality or power upon which man is dependent (and certainly this is one of the prime historical meanings of the term), it is easy to see why a "God is dead" theology and a "man is independent from nature" type of humanist philosophy are logically the same thing. The attempt of theologians in recent centuries to free their notion of God from the implications of scientific doctrine, because they did not like some of science's implications for their particular understandings of God, was dangerous. This attempt would be inherently disastrous for any credibility in God, if, as it turned out, more and more the scientific doctrines would shape the beliefs of people about what does in fact create, sustain, and rule human life.

I believe that a careful historical review will show that religions have in the past been most effective in beneficially shaping the feelings, emotions, and moral behaviors of a population when their beliefs about the ultimate and sovereign realities were consonant with the "science" of their day. Perhaps most of the scholarship and creative arts of the humanities today are, along with theology with which they share the function of interpreting to man his religious and moral values, suffering from a cultural lag behind the advances in knowledge made by the natural sciences. This is dangerous for the arts and the humanities, because they also become irrelevant and are rejected by a new generation raised in a culture whose beliefs about reality are incompatible with the traditional culture. The new generation cannot avoid beliefs shaped by new and different models of reality derived from the new sciences, even when their sentimental feelings reject certain views ascribed to those sciences. But it is more dangerous because humanity as a whole cannot long survive without institutions that adequately structure its beliefs, feelings, and its emotional and moral behavior. The crisis is going to be more threatening to the traditional culture of the humanities and theology as the psychosocial sciences become more closely integrated with the natural sciences, and this would seem to be a strong trend soon to be accomplished. Each year new discoveries are revealing man more and more to be a part of a single natural system. This threat to the humanities side of our two cultures with its mind-body dualism may at the same time be the salvation of mankind if it provides a new route to an integrated culture and a credible God.

Natural Selection and the Rebirth of Belief in a Suprahuman Power Ruling Man

In contrast with the above-mentioned dualistic views which portray man (and God) as significantly separate and independent from the natural world, the view that informs my attempt to develop a theology in the light of the sciences is a monistic view prevalent in the sciences. For theological as well as scientific purposes, I find congenial the notions of those scientists who find no absolute or ultimately real separation between human behavior and animal behavior, or between life and the lifeless matter and energy of the universe. This view flourishes more especially among those who have sought to understand behavior in terms of such disciplines as biochemistry; neurophysiology; cybernetic, homeostatic, information and general systems theory; behavioral psychology; and the like. These natural sciences have increasingly presupposed a faith in the continuity of all phenomena, in a monism (an integrated system rather than a dualistic or double nature) for explaining the world and life and men. This scientific hypothesis—that no phenomenon of human experience is in principle unconnectible in its history from other events and unexplainable in terms of some principles of invariance or lawful relationships—is very much akin to man's most primitive faith that the mysterious phenomena of experience are attributable to certain spirits or gods who characteristically behave in certain hypothesized ways to produce the otherwise unexplained phenomena. Furthermore, the strong tendency and phenomenal success of scientists, particularly in this century, to link all phenomena from astrophysics to life's genetic library and man's behavioral and perceptual programming to a common interconnected history and system of invariant principles to explain them, is astoundingly akin to the hypotheses in many cultures of some 2,500 years ago that all phenomena are caused by a single universal and sovereign principle or god. Twenty-five centuries later, if we might be expected to generate an equal realism about the determiner of our destiny, I suggest that our most credible, real, and useful doctrines of God now can be found in the most physicalistic doctrines of the creation, sustenance, and trends of the evolution of life.

But before we attempt to show the equivalence of the mighty acts of God in history with the operation of natural selection, we must be clear that natural selection operates in the higher aspects of human development, including what we commonly call culture and mind, which the dualists suppose are somehow independent from the body and from the material universe. I shall therefore concentrate on some contemporary scientific views of natural selection operating in the development of individuals, of their cultures, and of their brains, which is the objective name for that which structures or patterns what many call mind, thought, perception, experience, feeling, emotion, etc. Probably as we examine these selective processes which shape mind and personal experiences, feelings, values, and choices, as well as shape the history of the larger world in which we live, we shall see how close they are to what the traditional religions have called gods. In particular, those who have been enculturated in the Judaeo-Christian views will see how the characteristic operations of nature revealed by the sciences are quite close to the characteristics revealed in their tradition concerning the one, universal, omnipotent, sovereign creator of all that is, the definer of all that is good, building the kingdom of the good in history by surely destroying all that is evil.

Natural Selection in the Development of Human Individuals

It should be recalled that natural selection does not operate directly on the genes but operates on the phenotypes, or the living organisms.[11] Hence, it operates indirectly on the genotype. This genotype is the cumulated library of information which, when "read out" by a particular environment, informs the cell or the organism how to behave in the organized ways necessary for life. If the organism as thus directed behaves in the requisite ways to maintain life, the organism's cumulated internal genetic-heritage library is thus proven, tested, or selected by the organism as the library's viable product. Since the organism, instructed by this "fit" genotype, also, as a part of *its* fitness, behaves to replicate an edition of its genetic library in a new organism of the next generation, then this genetic information is selected. If such reproductive procreation of information is not successful, the genetic information is "selected out" or "selected against," by its failure to include a satisfactory procreation program as a part of the organism it produces. Hence, selection of the genotype is by selection of the phenotype that is able to survive long enough to procreate. There is an interesting parallel here to a familiar religious admonition. In the Christian tradition there is a caution that it is not sufficient to be hearers of the word or merely mouthers of the true word, but one must also be a doer of the word. The genotype is the word (for the precultural phenotype), but unless it becomes incarnate and active in the flesh, it is worthless and will not itself survive.

Thus, natural selection is operating, as Darwin wrote,[12] at every instant on every aspect of the interdependent parts of a living system, whether that system be as small as a cell or as large as the earth's biosphere. Human organisms are no exception to this rule, although they have some very exceptional sources of information and ways of adapting to the natural realities in order to maintain and enrich life. The following notes give some recently developed pictures of the nature of the forces acting to select and hence to shape or determine the destiny of men as they develop from conception to death.

The behavioral and life sciences have gone beyond the old debate on "nature versus nurture," because both nature and nurture are seen as aspects of a single interacting system. New ways of thinking, including systems analysis, have provided a formal way for avoiding the impasses and paradoxes of older ways of viewing things. The development of the living human being, begining at the point of conception, is now seen as the interaction between genetic heritage and environment. In computer jargon, it may be called a "readout" of the guidebook for living (encoded in the molecular patterns of the DNA of the genetic heritage or genotype) by the environment. It can be said that the genotype is a cumulative memory record of recipes for adaptations to a way of life that have thus far been successful among all prior constellations of the environmental niches of that life. Hence, it represents a cumulative wisdom for life selected by the historical events of the living systems in its world.

The immediately present environment of the DNA is a readout mechanism for reading the recipe book and making a human being. By a readout mechanism I mean any negative-feedback or cybernetic system in which the input of data or information (including the internal memory of previously acquired information) is transformed into some output response which directs or adapts the system to maintain or extend its already acquired goals. A readout mechanism may be as simple as a thermostat that reads out the dropping temperature and turns on the heater. The process is of the

same general form when a cook reads information from a
cookbook, from materials in the cupboard, and from internal
memory about certain goals and certain ways of behaving,
where the output is a delicious cake. The readout mechanism
whose output is a man, besides the very large recipe library in
the DNA, involves several levels, including (1) the cytoplasm
of the egg cell, (2) the internal physiology of the mother and
general behavior of the family, (3) the house, shelter, home,
village, or local habitat in which the family dwells and which for
humans includes the socially transmitted artifacts and habitual
patterns of human behavior of a family and society that represent a new mechanism for transmitting and storing recipes on
how to live—the cultural heritage going directly from brain to
brain, (4) the larger habitat of the country—the larger culture,
geography, climate, soil, etc.—where the home is found, and
(5) ultimately the larger ecosystem or habitat which includes
the sun and the cosmos.

The intimacy of the cosmic nature with life is often overlooked by those who are not close students of it. The nuclear
fusion of a star directly and indirectly influences life and its
development on earth and is an essential part of the positive
readout mechanism for the recorded memory in plant
genotypes and for men, for example, for eye development.
Moreover, cosmic characteristics provide the everlasting
source of the power and pattern that shapes all things. Its
power and pattern permeate all structures of the world and of
life from the creation of life long ago up through the present
and presumably, forevermore. The several stages or levels of
the environment are all simultaneously active to supply the
conditions for the interaction of the DNA recipe book with its
environment, which interaction is the "readout" of the genetic
code that programs or structures the development or behavior
of the organism. I shall point out a reverse or reciprocal
"readout" later—the readout of the environment by the
genotype. While scientific evidence for the details of the complex interaction of genotype and environment remains far from
complete, the new views and evidence for interaction and joint
selection of suitably matching genotypes and environments
seem to warrant an end of former worrying as to whether the
hen or the egg came first.[13]

In this picture of the developing person, it should never be overlooked that the genetic code, the genotype, is itself the heritage or memory of the successful interactions between living systems and environment produced over a time sequence of more than a billion years of evolution by innumerable trials and errors, always judged by natural selection. Thus, the genotype is itself essentially a symbolic codification of what the environment demands for life, which has been "read out' of a long history. Thus, the *genotype*, which is information for living that has been read out of the environment and recorded in nucleic acid by natural selection, is reciprocal to the *phenotype* (the body), which is a pattern of living being and activity that has been read out of the genotype by the immediate environment and incarnated in amino acid and other structures by natural selection. Since the genetic message is only transmitted when the succession of organisms instructed by it have been adapted successfully and continuously since it began, the message is an encoding of successful patterns of life in the environment, and hence can be regarded as a record of the environment. One could say that the DNA pattern is a condensed image of the environment internalized in cells to guide their life. The molecules of the genetic DNA chain differ from a randomly arranged chain of DNA molecules only in that they do in fact incorporate in a symbolic code a very precious heritage, memory, or register of information about how to live, derived from ages of experiences of evolving adaptations for life in the world.

It is a widely held hypothesis about animal and human development that, at every moment from the zygote or union of parental genes, through embryo, to death, "selection" is operating. That is, at every instant the production or behavior of the various chemicals by the natural interaction of genetic code and environing chemicals is such that the feedback information (which may involve simply the concentration of certain molecular structures) will shut off or turn on at the right times the proper releases of energy and the proper manufacture of one chemical structure or another so that a viable organism is developed and maintained.

The selection is always a matter of viability or survival—one could say *stability* of the open system; for, as soon as the molecular structures and behaviors within and around the cellular structures of life (and the organic structures and behaviors that they produce) fail to meet the multitudinous and complex requirements for the continuity of the organism within the environment, at that point the whole development is broken off and death occurs. If this developmental process fails to produce the required dynamic homeostasis at any point after birth (as in the case of failure to inhibit or prevent internal development of a certain type of destructive virus or bacterium or to regulate properly the internal temperature or food supply, etc.), the organism will die; that is, the *nature* of the situation removes the organism and its unadaptive behavior from the face of the world and from future history. Thus, nature (the physical nature of the interacting system) selects or weeds out bad or inadequate programs that are not adapted to life. The unadapted organism will cease; and, if it dies prior to its reproductive activities, its particular genotype will also be weeded out from the gene pool.

It should be noted that in primitive living systems, it is the "motherhood" or "fatherhood" of the general environment (the immediate ecosystem) that fosters or selects the development of the organism from the time the egg is fertilized or from the time it leaves protection by its organic parents. But in mammals, including man, the parental behavior of adult organisms becomes a vital part of the immediate environment of the embryo and infant, and hence of the selective process. In such cases, we note that parents, particularly the mothers, are genetically programmed to operate in ways protective of and nourishing to the development of their offspring. In any cases where this proper parental behavior has been inadequate, the infants die, and that is the end of that genetic line. Thus, selection operates to generate proper parental behavior, and parental behavior in turn selects the appropriate responses of the growing infant. Elaborate details of proper parental behavior are genetically programmed in many species. While only the larger outlines of parental behavior are genetically programmed in *Homo sapiens*, there are still millions of details to which cultural heritage has as yet contributed very little.

Natural Selection of the Culturetype

But, in addition to genetic programming of parental provision for children, individuals in human societies are also programmed by a tradition, a body of information, that is passed on, often more or less unconsciously at the most primitive levels, from parents, peer groups, and other instructors or shapers of the behavior that is characteristic in the society.

The cultural storage and replication of information are quite different from the ways in which the storage and replication of information are carried on in the genotype or genetic heritage. Yet a systems analysis shows equivalency of function. Moreover, the role of "selection by the natural consequences of the interacting systems" (which is a good way of saying "natural selection") is identical for the establishment of both the genetic and the cultural patterns.

Because I believe the role of natural selection in establishing the cultural pool of information and its transmission as part of the input that patterns structures and behaviors is the essence for a scientifically grounded understanding of the reality and relevance of a doctrine of God (understood as a system of forces that did create and does determine human destiny, and whose rules man must accept if he is to have life), I shall outline some of what I think are significant new understandings of the mechanisms of cultural evolution and of the operations of natural selection in determining the ultimate patterns of human behavior regardless of whether these patterns are fabricated in the genotype or in the culturetype or by what is involved for every human, the joint input of both.

The structures and behaviors of all living creatures are informed (caused or made into their particular patterns) by the interaction between two systems: their genetic heritage, or genotype, and their environment. The environmental system may be analyzed concurrently into several subsystems from cell cytoplasm to cosmos. Ultimately, in the scientific view that I espouse, there is no separation between man and the cosmos. As Harlow Shapley has said, "We have evidence of a truly wide Cosmic Evolution from hydrogen to *Homo*. . . . We have in Cosmic Evolution a fundamental principle of growth that affects the chemical atoms as well as plants and animals, the stars and nebulae, space-time and mass-energy. In brief, every-thing we can name, everything material and non-material, is involved. It is around this Cosmic Evolution that we might build revised philosophies and religions."[14] The ultimate "par-ent" and ultimate "culture" may properly be said to be the cosmos.[15]

In this production of a living creature, the environment is much more important as an informing or structure-causing agent than some traditional genetics has supposed.[16] The information in the DNA of the genotype is no more than is necessary to produce the living organism by interactions in an environment which is also rather highly structured and hence a source of part of the necessary information as well as of the necessary energies and materials for living systems. A genotype will not result in a living being except in its proper environ-ment. Genotypes are not effective apart from the special cytoplasm of an egg; eggs must be incubated at suitable temp-erature; free oxygen and water and other molecules must be supplied at appropriate energy levels; and human infants must be reared in a society which communicates suitable informa-tion if they are to become viable adults and to procreate a viable species.

While some of the machinery of transmission of cultural heritage may seem to be just the opposite from that of genetic information, a closer analysis of the systems will show that basically the same sort of thing is happening. In the transmis-sion of culture to determine the development of a child, the generating form, or pattern, or information is located outside the skin of the growing person, while the pattern of his genetic (DNA code) heritage is inside each of his hundred billion or so body cells. The structures or patterns of culture enter the individual only through his eyes, ears, and other organs for sensing his external environment. As noted above, the culture is a special subclass of the environment which is highly charged with information for how the receiver should develop or behave. But, while the DNA operates from the interior of the cell and the culture from outside the skin, a systems analyst can see that both the genotype and the culturetype are information inputs that structure the behavior of the growing and living person.

Natural Selection in the Brain

In higher animals, it is the brain that organizes behavior (I use "brain" to include the subsystems of the nervous system). Much of the information in the brain comes already prepared or "canned." The genotype gives it its basic structure and behavioral proclivities, although we should always keep in mind that the character of the egg cytoplasm, the embryonic environment, and the postnatal environment supplied by nature apart from culture always play an essential role in the structuring and behavior of the brain. But it is the large amount of cultural input into the human brain that makes man different from all other animals. Fortunately, most of this, like the genotypic information, also comes prepared, prefabricated, and ready for use.

At first, a human infant operates according to the dictates of a brain informed largely by the "canned" information of his genotype together with information acquired in a growth where environmental influences are very little and only indirectly informed by culture. The brain, and hence the child, performs in a very highly organized way to maintain the characteristic patterns or dynamic homeostasis of the organism. It may be said to resemble in general function the orderly operation of a very complex cybernetic-computer machinery. It is so well informed about what is necessary for life that it performs billions of very highly complex and delicately integrated life-building and life-maintaining tasks every second, most of them in patterns that do not reach consciousness or awareness until some scientific research discovers what is going on. But in general we have learned enough about the behavior of the brain and the resulting behavior patterns that are visible to all observers that many scientists are quite confident that the brain is the prime organizer of human behavior above the level of the genetically (and environmentally) programmed biophysical or chemical operations of the organism.

In addition to its largely genetically preprogrammed controls to keep the internal machinery of the organism running smoothly to produce its characteristic life, the brain provides a necessary map or model of the self in the external world. The map is made up out of the brain's abstractions from the contemporary and remembered input from the eyes and ears and other external sensory organs. The map is dependent upon the remarkable capacity, akin to that of the genotype, of memory and, further, upon the even more remarkable capacity to classify elements of its exceedingly complex memory record and current experience into a relatively small and manageable number of categories useful for defining behavioral responses proper for maintaining life. These categories may be said to be the abstractions of relatively invariant symbols of significant elements of the experienced history which, together with certain modifiers or quantifiers, provide a representation of the self and the world and the self's proper responses thereto such that life-sustaining behavior is the end result. The genotype, of course, is also such a map; but its capacity and its rate of modifiability are much more limited. The brain's map of self and world is built up from interactions of the brain with the total structures of the self and its relevant world, wherein selective mechanisms genetically built into the brain rapidly generate response patterns that are "successful" or "viable." Ultimately, of course, selection is made by whether or not the total life system is so adapted as to maintain itself in being as it interacts with its environment. The perceptual world of experience produced by the brain performs this necessary function or it will come to an end and cease to be. The prepared or already organized input patterns to the brain that produce the common categories of perception are representations of the energy and structure patterns characteristic of the organism's self and habitat for which the organism has sensory mechanisms.

These neurological abstract patterns or maps of self and the world are the stuff of which symbols are made, including the words of human language which are symbols of experiences that are readily communicable from man to man. A word is a symbol or code for a category of neurological pattern, and hence for an experiential or behavioral pattern like "red," or "round," or "run," or "rip." The brain's map of self and world is inextricably interlaced with the neurological patterns of words which are functionally isomorphic with the map, like the relation between the words or route numbers and the towns and roads on a map. The symbol system of words that constitute a language to label the map of the self and world also comes to the brain already prepared, "canned." Children do not have to invent language. The language comes already evolved out of hundreds and thousands of years of cultural evolution, selected for its efficacy in performing its tasks, which includes facilitating the internal processes of thinking and computing or anticipating the future as well as the communicating of "thought" from one brain to another. The language systems are remembered in brains (with help from such cultural artifacts as writing and books) and are transmitted by the human brain's capacities to remember and to relate or classify cultural symbol systems with its genetically and environmentally programmed map of self and the world. They are selected by their efficiency and usefulness in meeting the needs or wants of the population of a culture and hence by its viability as a subsidiary element of a culture and, in the long run, by the viability of the culture.

With the aid of the culturally evolved language systems, including mathematics and the sciences, the brain has increased capacity to revise and simplify its abstractions so as to provide ever better fits to the environment and ever better and simpler formulas for computing the future. The genotypes also do this in the collective gene pool of a population, but at a much greater cost and at a much slower rate. The evolutionary invention of the human brain as an agent for cultural evolution produced a new, less expensive, and more rapid instrument of evolution than the evolutionary invention of the DNA-structured genotype. The genotypes distributed in the population of a species can recombine their symbolic abstractions of life-structuring information by chance mutations and chance recombinations in sexually reproducing organisms. But this kind of learning mechanism is very costly in terms of time and death.

Computing the future is necessary for organisms that are required to adapt themselves suitably in a changing environment. The genotypes can and do compute the future insofar as the future is a simple projection of the past. They also provide for a variable and unpredictable future by providing within the population a statistical distribution of types, some of which are bound to meet the requirements of some likely set of future environmental demands. But brains and their capacity to provide symbolic maps of the world, which include logical-transformation operators (especially those of the sciences), can predict the future much faster and with less loss of life. When these maps and their transformation formulas can be remembered and transmitted as part of cultural patterns (languages, technologies, religions, sciences, etc.) within a population of people, successful cultural adaptations can become a valuable heritage like the genetic heritage in providing fairly surefire behavior for life in a more complex and faster-changing environment.

Hence, in human culture we find a new kind of heritage for life structure, based on the more rapidly adaptive reformability of memory possessed by brains than by genotypes. In brains, memory can be reformed (by "killing" or wiping out the previous pattern and substituting a new trial or mutation) several times a second and testing it several times a second for viability or selection in a moderately adequate or reliable model or map of the self and world internalized in the brain. Trial and error in the real world, as a method of evolution's prior search for better adaptations to the requirements for life, is much slower than trial and error in the brain because it requires the testing out of the whole organism, which takes a good deal of time. It is more costly since, if in the trials or mutations there must be a certain number of errors or deaths per successful adaptation, it will cost that many deaths of whole organisms (and of their genetic patterns) for each successful or adaptive trial. But in the case of trials by a modifiable model maker like the brain, where it is only the bad models which are "killed" and not the total mechanism for making the models, the cost is measured in terms of the time and energy taken to weed out bad models. This is relatively small.

In the brain, bad models can be weeded out very fast by fairly adequate internal selection processes. Internal selection is the first of the brain's programs of "natural selection" or screening for relevance. In a brain which has elaborate and well-tested maps of the self and world, this screening process (by unconscious and then by conscious, logical analysis of what fits and what is to be rejected) becomes a highly efficient and rapid program of "natural selection" in that, with a minimum cost of time and energy, higher levels are evolved.

The patterns of behavior that pass this first screening or selection, by natural processes in the brain mechanisms for surveying its current inputs in terms of its cumulated memory of past inputs, may then be tested more slowly and more surely in the "real world" when the brain selects its best internal selection as a program for test through behavior of the organism operating in the "real" world. If the baby's hand misses the rattle or if his mouth fails to find the wanted and needed food, his brain will recompute and try again. But even this test or selection by the "real world" is much faster than waiting for a new generation from a genetic mutation. Moreover, the mutability of the brain means that nature selects against or weeds out only the wrong behaviors and not necessarily the whole organism.

Natural Selection in a Community of Brains

Human culture also has the advantage of multiple simultaneous trials or mutations in its seeking of viable response patterns to the requirements of the general environment or habitat for life. In a society of individuals, many brains can be simultaneously searching for better solutions of human adaptation. If one man invents a moderately successful way of flying, another may invent another, and the most economic or successful adaptation will finally be selected by the nature of the circumstances.

It should be noted that not only can cultural evolution be speeded up by multiplying the number of trials by the number of the population making trials, but the finally "selected" successful adaptation can immediately be spread throughout the whole population. This multiplies the beneficial spread of success by the number of the population. This is possible because brains are modifiable, and all the people who made the wrong, unsuccessful, or nonselected trials can immediately adopt the successful adaptation found or discovered by only one of their number. To make this possible, brains must not only be modifiable, but they must be able to receive a communication of the successful adaptation. Among the world's artistic inventors or creators and in the world's technical laboratories, thousands of aborted trials are made for every successful invention of a new poem, picture, pill, machine, or other cultural artifact that may be valuable for human life. But the successful outcomes are communicated and become available to all, not only to those who tried and failed, but even to those who never tried to solve that particular problem of finding a better adaptation. In earlier kinds of evolutionary adaptation by means of many trials (polymorphism of genotypes in a population), each losing trial meant a costly death to a whole organism. In human culture, all trials and even all "dummies" who are not even playing the game can ultimately win because brains can be modified by communications of successful new adaptations.

Another example of the efficiency of human culture in the task of adapting to newer and higher levels of organization to live more successfully in wider and wider ranges of environmental circumstances is that of the social division of labor. The problem of inventing a single kind of flying machine, for instance, may be subdivided among whole groups of men drawing on information accumulated in various departments of the cultural heritage. A good example is the input from tens of thousands of men and many hundreds of special cultural disciplines that landed men on the moon. This speeded up the development of the possibility of landing on the moon in less than a decade from the time of the decision to do so. Left to isolated and random or unorganized applications of science by individual men, or to very small numbers of them working together, the project might have taken longer than the evolution of culture from the invention of the wheel to its application in the horseless carriage. Left to natural selection of genetic information, it would have taken more time than the earth has been in existence.

One should keep in mind that it was natural selection, however, that structured man's moon flight. As in the case of the operation of the individual brain, the first screening by natural selection was by imaginative games played internally in an interlinked net of brains encultured with operable models of the structures and behavioral laws of nature: of gravity, of motion, of men, etc. Individuals and groups among these scientists and engineers selected certain of these "plays with symbols" as winners at the theoretical level. A second stage was in more expensive testing of more "realistic" models. The final selection, as always, is that made by the ultimately "real nature," the nature of the total factors involved when men actually landed on the moon. The selective process weeded out imaginative inventions that the inventor or his colleagues found were contradicted by any already known facts or theories, weeded out partial physical models that failed when tried, weeded out actual moon landing programs that did not sufficiently meet the full range of requirements laid down by the ultimate realities of the situation. The modern scientific maps of man and his world, and the technologies that are derived from them, provide human culture with its most advanced mechanisms of adaptation, of seeking and finding new and more advanced ways to thrive in the "real" or "natural" world which is the ultimate judge of all that lives.

Thus, for rapidity and multiplicity of trials (mutations) and rapidity and multiplicity of testing them for viabliity in the real world (nature's selection), probably nothing in the evolution of life on earth has yet come to equal the system that we call human cultural evolution. This depends upon a population of brains each of which receives a treasured rich sample from three sources of heritage. The human infant's brain becomes the memory center for information input from three sets of heritages: (1) the input from a highly structured genotype that is a randomly selected variant of the highly structured human gene pool, unsuccessful variants of which have been largely weeded out in the past by natural selection, that is, by the natural lack of those forms that are not adapted to successful continuation (homeostasis) or reproduction; (2) input from a random sample of a fairly stable and habitable world or habitat, unsuccessful variants of which have been weeded out by the fact that inhospitable habitats for the existence of either the parents or the offspring are quickly weeded out by their failure to tolerate parents or offspring; and (3) input from a random sample of a human culturetype, which is a complex structuring of the general environment or habitat into a *human* ecological niche by the memory and consequent activities of the brains of parents and other members of the infant's society, the inhospitable or nonviable forms of this culturetype having been weeded out by the relative failure to be reproduced. The brain is structured and hence it operates (and the whole being thus operates) according to these three sources of memory, which are all aspects of a single evolving cosmos. In particular, the developing brain involves interactions of these three sources from which it is the task of the brain itself (as directed by its genetically structured memory) to select out and remember (and hence to utilize) some viable patterns that integrate from all three sources the proper response patterns for life. Natural selection is the name for the failure of erroneous (and hence unstable) conclusions or patterns to reproduce, to repeat, to survive.

Culturetypes may be viewed both from the perspective of the society and from the perspective of the individual person. From the point of view of the society as a whole, the culturetype is analogous to the genotype, and it reorders or reorganizes the behavior of individual persons or groups of them so as to make a viable society. From the point of view of the individual, the culturetype becomes ingrained in his central nervous system by the reinforcement or inhibition of his initial behaviors as directed by his genetically structured needs or desires and patterns for attaining them. The cultural system knows how to modify and elaborate genetically programmed behavioral systems by operating on the reward and punishment systems for reinforcing or repressing behavior already provided by the genotype. Pleasure and pain (or desires for more or less of something) were provisions of the genotype that more than a billion years ago were selected as necessary for life: it was necessary for the living being to shun the noxious and incorporate the nourishing elements from the environment. Each living unit had to be informed how to avoid evil and seek and attain the good in its environment. It thus generated mechanisms for seeking and avoiding.

It was a natural consequence that other organisms of either the same or a different species would be able to manipulate a given organism by manipulating that organism's seeking and avoiding mechanisms. Thus has nature selected programs for motivating sexual reproduction or the viability of the species by endowing the opposite sexes with genetically programmed mechanisms that make sexual recombination most attractive. An interspecific example is the genetically programmed machinery of a bee to sting which keeps men and beasts away from the bee's nest, at least until they learn how to avoid the consequence of a bee sting. It is in such ways by which other members of his society operate on his desire mechanisms that the human individual is motivated to operate according to the mores or customs of the society in which he has been enculturated. The brain of every human individual is thus programmed by his culture from outside as well as by his genotype from inside.

By providing a common culturetype that informs, shapes, and motivates the various individual men within it, common cultures in fact make "brothers" of men, brothers having a common "soul" or heritage insofar as a culturetype has become in fact a common pattern of a society's heritage. As cultural evolution advances and men have larger and larger portions of their nature structured by a common culture, they become more and more like brothers; in fact, they become more and more closely related as members of a common body or social organism.

It has been argued by some scientists[17] that the only successful and complex societies among animals (apart from man) have been among the insects, and that this is possible only because the whole society is made up out of and selected by the mechanisms of essentially a common genotype. It has been argued that natural selection of interbreeding genetic populations cannot produce self-sacrificial behavior of one individual on behalf of other individuals of a different genetic line in the same population. Selection operates by the number of survivors, and if a genetic line produced individuals that gave up their lives for a second genetic line, the second genetic line would eventually be all that would be surviving. The different social castes in insect societies are differentiations made by differential information input from the environment during ontogeny, and hence the social specializations found here may be said to come not from a difference in genotype but by postnatal instruction. This postzygotic, extragenotypic differentiation of function is similar to that of a colony of cells that make up an organism. They all have the same genotype, but are given different structures and functions by information input from outside during ontogeny. Marked social differentiation of function is not found in higher animals, such as mammals, it is argued, because evolution did not find sufficiently powerful nongenetic ways for differentiating functions that all serve a common social goal to the extent that one individual will deny himself for the welfare of the total society.

The cooperating society of some hundred billion cells of the human body, that make me what I am and you what you are, is the product of a single genotype, a single egg. One theory suggests that each of the cells of the developing human is instructed in slightly different ways by the slightly different conditions of its immediate habitat (which, of course, includes other cells) so that the result is not a population of a few billion competing and quarreling individuals constituting a number of aggregates or nations all at war with one another, as is sometimes the threat among human populations; but the human body is a population of highly differentiated but faithfully cooperating cells several times more numerous than the human population of the world. Each cell's operations are so delicately subservient to the general welfare of the total organism that you by and large find yourself to be a quite wonderfully one, single, integrated being. A cancer is a case where certain cells take an independent stand for their own "tribe" or "nation."

In human populations, the genetic blockage to making a cooperative group out of varied and competing individuals from a polymorphic gene pool has been at least partially and potentially overcome by the provision of a common heritage through a common culturetype. The different informational input of a culture into a human population is capable of turning similar organisms into different social roles, such as tinker, tailor, cowboy, sailor, doctor, lawyer, Indian chief. But in *Homo* this has been accomplished in spite of the fact that the human population is already highly differentiated in its genetic structures, which is not true for insects in insect societies—a matter that indicates something very special about the human genotype and its interdependence or symbiosis with a culturetype. In the past, certain religious and other cultural transmitters of common values have unified populations by producing a community of common aspiration, trust, and cooperation (even self-sacrificial behavior) throughout a numerous population of organisms whose genotypes would not be able to accomplish this without the added cultural input.

Natural selection, as I have been insisting, operates in establishing the seed, memory, or heritage of a culture, and an interesting question immediately arises as to why it is possible for nature to select a culturally programmed trait in which a man may be programmed to serve other men at sacrifices to himself while it may be impossible to do this by natural selection of genotypic programs. The answer is that the culturetype is common to each member of the whole population of a society, like the common genotype that provides the possibility for self-sacrificial social behavior in the social insects or in the cells of a single organism.

The selection among the social insects of traits that are useful in permitting the total society to survive at the cost of a specialized duty by some caste, say soldiers, which means that they cannot farm for food and must be dependent on others in the society for the food, and which may mean that they have to give up their lives while those they protect do not, has been made possible, it is suggested, by the fact that the common genotype and procreation system for all castes means that the sacrificing of some of them is not in the least lethal for that genotype, even though it may be lethal for many individual soldiers in the society. On the contrary, because of the brave and sacrificial defense of the soldier, the society may be more likely to survive, and hence that soldier's genotype, which is identical with the one that shapes the society, would be selected.

The same is true for human culturetypes, even though it may not be for human genotypes. Since the culturetype is common to a total human society—the way the genotype is common to a total insect society—then the bravery of soldiers, the hard work of farmers, or the devotion of all those who direct their labors to the commonweal may produce a society that is much better able to survive under certain conditions than one which had cowardly soldiers, or lazy farmers, or indifferent citizens. The thriving of the community or society as a whole is what selects a culture. (I am here leaving out of consideration that different societies may have gene pools of different character and that this also may enter into the viability of the society, since I am here discussing only culturetype and not genotype.) In this situation, as in the case of insect societies, it matters little how dangerous or personally disadvantageous may be the lives of those in certain special occupations, as long as they can be motivated (by the culturetype operating in conjunction with the given genotypes and habitats in the population) to their task and as long as the danger to or loss of these individuals does not adversely affect any other aspects of the community's well-being. If a certain culture will produce a richer life for a greater number, it will continue to attract people at the expense of other cultures that may have produced more poverty, less opportunity and interest, etc.

An interesting example of how the life of a culture is partially separated from human genetic factors and is selected by the quality of the culture even though it may be genetically inferior is the reported fact that in the last few thousand years the reproduction rate of the human gene pool has been lower in cities than in rural areas. But the urban subculture attracts young people away from the rural areas, so that in fact the population of cities has been maintained or increased in spite of their smaller reproduction rate. Another interesting example to show the independence of culturetype from genotype is the fact that the various cultures of the world are buying or adopting the scientific-technological culture of the West because of its advantages to them compared with their previous cultural tradition. There are many problems for us and for them here, but we cannot treat them in this paper.

Some Cautions and Conclusions

I must briefly mention some matters that may be frightening, and some properly so. There are several dangers in programming by a culture. Some of these fears have been portrayed in part by such writers as Aldous Huxley in his *Brave New World*. But what most people do not realize is that society has for millennia been programming the behavior of each new generation through its culturetypes at least as completely as the programming portrayed by such fearful writings. But the results on the whole have been beneficial and have caused societies to flourish. A number of psychosocial scientists have in the past few decades been impressed with this, and their literature is a sobering and also heartening reminder of what tremendous gifts for enriching animal life comes from social imprinting, conditioning, reinforcement, and other programs for inducing certain behavior patterns.[18] Every local culture, every language, every religion programs its population. We are as unable to avoid most of our being shaped by a culturetype as we are unable to avoid our genetic heritage. We can do little better in choosing our cultural "parents" than in choosing our genetic parents.

But the fearsome tales of *Brave New World* and *1984* and the like do not reveal the heart of the matter. The important point to note is that in any system of competing cultures or subcultures natural selection is continuously weeding out evil. The wicked do in fact perish, and the righteous are rewarded, if we take reward to mean that their "good" or "fit" patterns of life will survive. If you trust in the Lord of natural selection, you need not fear that the wicked will triumph. You will not join the alarmists in conjuring up mountainous threats out of molehill dangers inherent in selfish ignoramuses that have always populated human societies. Natural selection is certain to crush any competing individual or group that fails to follow the rules which the ultimate nature of things has defined as right or necessary for survival.

In fact, this is perhaps the primary point of this paper: that the sciences confirm what many of the traditional religious doctrines have long declared, that there is a superior power that creates and ordains life and judges, rules, or selects—punishes or eliminates what is wicked and rewards or causes to survive what is good. The notion that man is self-made or in control of his destiny and the notion that human desires or wants are necessarily the primary source or criterion of values are as wrong according to a scientific doctrine of man as they are according to many of the traditional religious doctrines. What is most important here is to note that this statement applies not only to man's emergence out of his earlier strata of cosmic chemicals and of animal nature, but equally to everything that happens at the highest levels of operation of the human brain and culture.

In cultural programming, what man needs to fear is not so much the wickedness of human tyrants or manipulators as it is his own (and his companions') failure to recognize that there is a sovereign power and authority, and his own failure to adopt or adapt to this authority. The clever schemes of the wicked to manipulate their fellow beings for their own private self-interest are statistically as impossible as is the survival of a genotype that does not produce a viable organism of cooperating cells. Cancerous (selfish) cells kill the genotype that programs them if they operate prior to natural selection's deadline. The problem of evil and evil men is a problem where a scientific doctrine of man looks to me to be very equivalent to the best religious literature. But the significant first step in finding a correct and viable doctrine of man for our own welfare or salvation is our recognition of the reality or nature which far transcends all men in power and which weeds out the inadequate and favors those better adapted to that nature's ultimate requirements. As long as a significant population of men have freedom to adapt to the requirements of natural selection or the Lord, wicked men pose no serious threat to the coming of the Lord's kingdom of enriched life upon the earth.

This does not mean that men have no obligation to seek the good and to destroy the evil, for they are agents of the Lord or natural selection in this process. What is important is that they need not fear that evil or inviable patterns will triumph in the end or survive. It is of the very nature of men that they will be continuously reinforced to seek the good and shun evil by pleasure and pain administered by selection pressures genetically from within, and from without by selection pressures from their habitat and their culturetype (social pressures). "Thou has made us for thyself, O God, and our hearts are restless until they find their rest in thee," as Saint Augustine put it. The grace here revealed by our understanding of an omnipotent natural selection is that we do not need to get panicky when we and our fellowmen make their inevitable mistakes in their necessarily imperfect search for the patterns of behavior that natural selection requires.

However, one serious problem for continued operation of natural selection in human culture should immediately concern us if we wish to see the Lord's kingdom of enriched life come to pass on earth, and that is that we must ensure that our system of life remains open or reasonably free to try or search for novel patterns of life, even at considerable cost. We can never avoid the punishment of natural selection's rule, for behavior that fails to meet nature's requirements for life is lethal, and our innovations now and in the future carry some of this risk of being detrimental, as they always have in past evolution. For this reason, we need to distribute risks, and not put all our eggs in one basket. A single, rigid, inflexible world culture might be the most dangerous situation we could put ourselves in. Evolution requires the freedom of different approaches in the search for true adaptations, different trials, many of which must be errors. We have to tolerate error and evil as a price for advancement of life. This is the way nature or the sovereign "Lord" has arranged things. As we come to an age in which we must have some degree of uniformity in world culture (for we are now in reality an interdependent population forming a world society), we must at the same time see to it that tolerance for variance, for difference, for error, is built into our system—else we leave ourselves open only to the *negative* judgment of natural selection: death for man on earth.

The seeming paradox of evil in a world ruled by an omnipotent and just sovereign power—a problem that remains the same whether you call the power "God" or "natural selection"—dissolves when we understand the scientific revelations of the dynamic character of evolving systems of life. Viewed as a necessary part of the program toward the ultimate triumph of good, the "errors" or variation become necessary, and hence good rather than evil, for generating life. Viewed as a part of present human desires, themselves necessarily partly in error, the error is then evil rather than good. The only salvation for man is a cultural transmission of truths that enable him to transcend his limited private views and desires and to adopt a longer-range, more divine perspective, wherein he may recognize his present imperfection and suffering as a necessary element toward the long-range good guaranteed by God. Animals already behave with this "courage" and "hope" in the face of the same necessary danger and death, since their genotypes are adapted to this reality of life. In *Homo sapiens*, the genotype does not very adequately provide such courage and hope. For shaping man's morale and morals, as for his technology or language, man's genetic information must be supplemented by an adapted body of cultural information which we call religion.

Let us review how both culturetype and genotype find new and better adaptations and how the better adaptations are selected and maintained. My review of some recent notions of the natural causes of human behavior indicates that adaptive behavior patterns may be initiated by chance or random behavior at the level either of DNA molecules or of brain cells. The organized system of billions of DNA molecules of the genotype is a very different mechanism from the organized system of billions of brain cells. But both systems remember or store information learned in the process of living. They use this information to direct or organize the life behavior of the cells or organisms. Both systems when suitably stimulated by circumstances in their environment (habitat) will guide and organize activities that maintain life. By negative-feedback mechanisms, they correct mistakes and correctly organize the life programs of which they are the long-enduring core, or we might call it the "soul." Both systems of remembering are capable of change or mutation; they are capable of having their mistakes corrected and of discovering better ways of living, although this is an expensive statistical process requiring large numbers of independent units, most of which have to be sacrificed in order that a few are enabled to hit the mark of a new, successful adaptation. It is something like the "wastefulness" of shotgun ammunition, only a fraction of which will hit the target. What is central for this essay is to note that the eventual historical form or pattern of structure-behavior taken by man's "soul" (any of the persisting records or memories of experience distilled in DNA, culturetypes, etc.) and hence by human persons (phenotypes) is not decided or determined by the memory mechanism or even by the particular memory content, but by whether or not the remembered information has discovered ways of behaving that are in fact capable of keeping the open living system in being. This is what the terms "viable" and "adapted" mean; ability to behave so as to meet the requirements placed by the nature of the environment and the nature of all the detailed organization of the open living system so as to keep the living system in being—surviving, stable. Nature is sovereign and selects or judges the products of either of these systems of learning and memory.

Remembering that the nature that selects what shall live is the total nature, including the ingredients and behaviors inside the living system as well as the ingredients and dynamics of the environment—that is, selection is the stability or continuity of an evolving ecological niche—we have already noted that the nature that selects or judges is a complex operation of many subsystems all of which have to be kept integrated so that the life system maintains its stability or dynamic homeostasis.

We have also noted that living systems, including men, are the products of the history of nature, of a long history of evolving patterns, which modern science traces back to a time before there was any life. Thus, the nature that selected man is ultimately to be traced to the nature described by the physical sciences—the basic nature of the earth and cosmos as it was before there was any subject matter for biological or psychological science.

As is increasingly demonstrated in the history of the sciences in the twentieth century, various aspects of biology are being illuminated by physics, including the machinery and behavior of genetics in terms of the nature and operations of DNA molecules; the machinery and behavior of the brain in terms of electrical, chemical, and molecular operations; the machinery and behavior of glands and muscles in terms of physical chemistry; and so on. Hence, we may say that the nature of the physical world provides useful explanations about many of its subsystems, including the structures and dynamics (behavior) of living systems. This even applies to describing the way men think and feel, which, when understood in terms of the electromagnetic structures and energies of brain cells and their molecular subunits, is a description of a very complex physical subsystem. Thus, even the description of the dynamic equilibria of events inside the membrane of a living system, as well as of the dynamics of events in the environment, may be a description in terms of the same nature which physics has helped us to understand.[19]

The *nature* that selects any of its subsystems is now understood in terms of nature's invariances. Invariances are

unchanging conditions and laws according to which we find the
more changing phenomena of nature to be operating. The laws
of physics are only a special class of the invariances revealed to
the human mind and confirmed by human experience. In the
history of human thought, among the earliest and most comprehensive systems of abstractions of invariance were those of
primitive myths and theologies, which gave the names of gods
to the sources of the invariant and powerful forces or laws
which man had to obey if he was successfully to adapt to life.

One of the most comprehensive recent pictures of the total
system of nature as it applies to the evolution of life and human
life in my opinion is that presented by J. Bronowski in his
"New Concepts in the Evolution of Complexity."[20] The progress in the evolution of life may be understood as the attain-
ment of successive levels of increasing complexity which,
according to nature or nature's laws, are permissible, stable, or
viable when attained. One might say, in this picture, that these
viability or stability levels are potentials (preexistent or prolep-
tic) in nature. At successive stages in history, they may be
attained provided the conditions that nature requires for their
coming into being are met. In evolution these conditions have
been met by chance, that is, by the random variations or trials
that nature's energy sources make available. However, the
selection of one or more of the trials and the *rejection* of most of
the others *are not by chance, but by the requirements for
stability inherent in the nature of the interacting elements, inherent in nature.*

This same principle is true whether we are talking about the
random fluctuations of protons and electrons that are bound
under certain conditions to stabilize as hydrogen or under
other conditions as helium plus solar radiation, etc., or whether
we are talking about random searchings of men for better ways
of ordering human life that are bound together under certain
conditions to stabilize as one of a limited number of highly
complex organizations of hunting-and-gathering cultures, of
agricultural cultures, or of worldwide technical-industrial
societies, etc. Selection by nature is another way of saying that
nature offers only a very restricted number of ways in which
systems can persist, be stable, homeostatic, or alive. "Narrow is
the gate and strait is the way that leadeth unto life."

Summary

In brief, I have been suggesting: (1) "Natural selection" may be considered as a succession of stability levels existing in *nature* which are the *natural* outcome according to *natural* laws of the interaction of *natural* systems, even under random energies or motions. (2) Natural selection of *living systems* is no different except for the fact that living systems are a special class of the natural phenomena of open systems that are stable patterns because they are structured or defined by special memories and homeostatic (cybernetic) mechanisms to maintain or increase a degree of order or organization which is not possible in general and particularly not possible in closed systems where it is forbidden by the second law of thermodynamics. (3) Natural selection of living systems requires a "memory" sufficiently stable in its pattern to reconstruct or replicate essentially the same kind of organism or behavior, but sufficiently flexible (changeable or mutable) to allow for at least a small proportion of errors which are necessary as trials to find (to learn) a better adaptation of the living system to the demands and opportunities of nature. (4) Natural selection of the memory structures (including genotypes and habitats) is indirect by means of the selection (i.e., the viability, stability, or homeostasis) of the living structures (phenotypes) they reproduce. (5) Natural selection at the level of human life involves three quite distinguishable sets of memory or information: two of them (genotypes and habitats) are common to all other kinds of life on earth, and the third, or culturetype, is a special structuring of the habitat by parents and society and gives man his uniqueness among living species on earth. (6) Natural selection of the heritage of culturetypes involves selection of the memory or information patterns stored in the brain, but it is information which is transmitted to the brain from outside the brain rather than from inside the brain as is its information or heritage from the genotype.

In spite of the fact that Charles Darwin may have denied that he was replacing the term "God" with "Natural Selection,"[21] I will quote from his *Origin of Species* (early in chap. 4) to show how closely the notion of natural selection does resemble the

God of Western religious tradition (and I think it can be shown to be equivalent in many respects to most concepts of the ultimate powers):

It may be said that natural selection is daily and hourly scrutinizing throughout the world, every variation, even the slightest; rejecting that which is bad, preserving and adding up all that is good; silently and insensibly working, whenever and wherever opportunity offers, at the improvement of each organic being in relation to its organic and inorganic conditions of life.

I do not find this very far from the following, which was written more than two thousand years prior:

O Lord, thou hast searched me, and known me. Thou knowest my downsitting and mine uprising; thou understandest my thought afar off. Thou compassest my path and my lying down, and art acquainted with all my ways. . . . Search me, O God, and know my heart: try me, and know my thoughts: and see if there be any wicked way in me, and lead me in the way everlasting.[22]

NOTES

1. Hudson Hoagland and Ralph Burhoe, eds., *Evolution and Man's Progress* (New York: Columbia University Press, 1961); see especially pp. 67-69, in the chapter by Julian H. Steward and Dimitri Shimkin.

2. Theodosius Dobzhansky, *Mankind Evolving* (New Haven, Conn.: Yale University Press, 1962).

3. B. F. Skinner, "The Phylogeny and Ontogeny of Behavior," *Science* 153 (1966): 1205-13.

4. George Gaylord Simpson, *The Meaning of Evolution,* rev. and abr. ed. (New York: Mentor Books, 1949; New Haven, Conn.: Yale University Press, 1951), p. 95; or C. H. Waddington, *Towards a Theoretical Biology* (Chicago: Aldine Publishing Co., 1968), 1:19.

5. See Waddington, pp. 288 ff, and elsewhere; also, Ralph Wendell Burhoe, "Commentary on J. Bronowski's 'New Concepts in the Evolution of Complexity,' " *Zygon* 5 (1970): 36-40.

6. Clyde Kluckhohn, "The Scientific Study of Values and Contemporary Civilization," *Zygon* (1966): 230-43; see especially p.236. It is common knowledge, or at least widely reported, that the sciences are low on the educational totem pole.

7. C. P. Snow, *The Two Cultures and the Scientific Revolution* (New York: Cambridge University Press, 1960).

8. An interesting commentary on Darwin's natural selection is to be found in Garrett Hardin's *Nature and Man's Fate* (New York: Holt, Rinehart & Winston, 1959), pp. 59-60.

9. Stow Persons, *Free Religion* (Boston: Beacon Press, 1947), p. 64.

10. See, for example, Oscar Riddle's evaluation of this in his "The Emergence of Good and Evil," *Zygon* 2 (1967): 34-42.

11. Ralph Wendell Burhoe, "What Specifies the Values of the Man-made Man?" *Zygon* 6 (1971): 224-46.

12. Charles Darwin, *The Origin of Species* (1859), early in chap. 4 on natural selection; it is on p. 97 of the Harvard Classics edition.

13. The computer-language description of living systems as cybernetic systems processing information has grown out of many studies in the past two or three decades about these systems; see, for instance, the various books and papers in this field by A. M. Turing, Norbert Weiner, W. Ross Ashby, Warren McCulloch, John von Neumann, J. Z. Young, Kenneth Boulding, Karl W. Deutsch, Garrett Hardin, and a multitude of others.

14. Harlow Shapley, "Life, Hope, and Cosmic Evolution," *Zygon* 1 (1966): 281.

15. Further details on this notion will be found in J. Bronowski's "New Concepts in the Evolution of Complexity: Stratified Stability and Unbounded Plans," *Zygon* 5 (1970): 18-35, and Burhoe's comment thereon (n. 5 above), especially pp. 39-40.

16. See Herbert A. Simon, *The Sciences of the Artifical* (Cambridge, Mass.: M.I.T. Press, 1969), especially p. 25: "A man, viewed as a behaving system, is quite simple. The apparent complexity of his behavior over time is largely a reflection of the complexity of the environment in which he finds himself." This book has many rich insights for anyone who wishes to understand the operation of selection in "learning" of all kinds, from genotypes, to brains, to computers.

17. E.g., Donald T. Campbell, "Variation and Selective Retention in Socio-cultural Evolution," *General Systems* 14 (1969): 69-85. See also G. C. Williams, *Adaptation and Natural Selection* (Princeton, N. J.: Princeton University Press, 1966), on which Campbell's argument is based.

18. Cf. C. H. Waddington, *The Ethical Animal* (New York: Atheneum Press, 1961), for a good review; B. F. Skinner's *Science and Human Behavior* (New York: Macmillan Co., 1953) is a basic text.

19. There is a vast literature on the understanding of living systems in terms of physical parameters by authors ranging from A to Z. As a beginning for persons not acquainted with this, I would highly recommend various books by Isaac Asimov and Dean E. Wooldridge.

20. Bronowski (n. 15 above), pp. 18-35.

21. Darwin (n. 12 above).

22. Psalms, chap. 139.

5

The Concepts of God and Soul in a Scientific View of Human Purpose*

This symposium on science and human purpose seeks to make some sense and perhaps offer some practical solutions to an ominous cloud of anomie and absurdity advancing over the horizon of human perspectives. As man's view of himself and his world and his powers to transform them are enhanced by the sciences, his traditional convictions about his worth, meaning, and purpose in the scheme of things are disintegrating. This is hitting hardest among the youthful, better-educated, and more economically advanced and sensitive elements of the world population. But it is becoming widespread enough to portend societal and personal breakdowns of horrible dimensions.

Civilization does not seem to make sense to many, and by some it is rejected as absurd. Some respond by means of genetically programmed escape mechanisms, ranging from angry attack and disruption to opting out, with or without the aid of drugs. Youth are led to this rebellion by the valid critiques of the ills of civilization often made by their elders; the existential poets have pointed to the absurdity of our spiritual position, while the Club of Rome predicts practical and material doom.[1] There are many doomsday scenarios of man's spiritual and material condition that have been produced

*This paper was presented to the Symposium on Science and Human Purpose held at the Institute on Man and Science at Rensselaerville, N.Y., in October of 1972, by the Institute on Religion in an Age of Science. It was first published in *Zygon* 8(3-4): 412-442, September-December 1973.

since *The Waste Land, Brave New World,* and *1984,* including *No Place to Hide, The Making of a Counter Culture, The Greening of America,* and *Where the Wasteland Ends.*[2]

I take it that in this symposium we are calling for various disciplines of human understanding to illuminate the problem and help us make sense of it. I understand that by "purpose" we are referring to human aims or goals. I shall include not only the aims and goals of which a man is consciously aware, but also aims or goals that he seeks because of internal mechanisms of which he may be largely or even completely unconscious, such as his purpose to provide variation of human genotypes by means of bisexual recombinations. I shall also include among human purposes those that are real enough but only temporary and those aims and goals which may be self-defeating, such as desires that may have lethal consequences, as well as those which may be self-enhancing. In human purposes we include, of course, those aims and goals that give a man meaning and hope and guide his behavior to a successful outcome in the midst of confusing and perplexing conditions that surround him.

I take it that we are looking at these purposes scientifically because we suppose scientific theory may contain as sound and valid a picture as we can find today. I take it that we are seeking to relate the scientific insights to the older cultural, philosophic, and religious traditions since those traditions have shaped viable societies in the past and may contain at least some hints of what we must do to shape viable societies in the present or future. This respect for the prescientific tradition is itself a mark of scientific respect for history and for the wisdom in what the evolutionary process has produced so far. While the more radical revolts on the disturbed frontiers of contemporary culture may reject a whole tradition because it has proved a failure in some respects—as communism and Freudianism rejected Christianity—a truly scientific approach to repairing the present cultural breakdown would seek to understand more fully the complex nature of the once viable and flourishing systems that are breaking down and thus come to know more fully the nature of the system that needs to be repaired or improved. We understand that in cultural as well as genetic evolution it becomes increasingly impossible to build viable complex living systems from scratch, but it is usually possible to evolve one by making slight alterations or extensions on some already viable system.

I think that on the whole the members of this symposium share a faith both in the scientific approach to valid knowledge and in the wisdom of the more highly evolved systems of human beliefs and institutions that thus far have shaped human purposes. I think we share the conviction that light from the sciences may provide some corrections or repairs to the traditional systems and at the same time provide some basic support or reinforcement for their fundamental wisdom. We think that we can move toward a new illumination of meaning and purpose that will be helpful for motivating more effective ethical decisions as well as helpful for satisfying the deep needs for hope, courage, and integrity on the part of the individual actors in the human drama.

I take it further that we are considering the problem of human purpose in its broadest dimensions, considering in broad outline not only the already existing motives, goals, and directions embodied in individual and social systems, but also, and perhaps in more detail, the long-range place or role of man in the scheme of things. This last leads to examination of man's ultimate aims, goals, concerns, or purposes and hence relates our problem to the realm of religion, theology, and "old-fashioned" philosophy.

In many advanced centers of contemporary culture, the scientific and rational approach to questions of human meaning and purpose are as much spurned as are those of the traditional religions. The views of Theodore Roszak are representative of what I mean.[3] For him science is a devil, and, while he turns to certain hopes for some meaning that may be found in man's primitive religious resources, I gather he does not look upon the higher religions as very helpful. It is a curious phenomenon, and one for us to ponder carefully, that in much Western humanism the higher religious traditions are largely rejected on the grounds that scientific evidence has made religious beliefs seem incredible—hence spiritually and morally ineffective. Yet at the same time the sciences, which have provided a higher credibility about the "real" or "true" nature of things, are rejected as being inherently destructive devils incapable of being useful for developing new moral or religious "truth"! We can agree with Roszak in understanding the destructive effect upon religious beliefs of certain popularizations of the meaning of "science"; but instead of finding the sciences to be devils, I believe we can show that the scientific revelations may be saving angels, for enhancing our understanding not only of the realities underlying medicine and other technologies, but also of the realities underlying man's long-range aims, goals, or purposes.

In the Western world, according to Toynbee, the Judaeo-Christian religion had lost its effective hold by the seventeenth century.[4] In the minds of many its place has been taken by various "heresies" or humanistic, social, or national philosophies.[5] I wish to note briefly why I shall not try to deal with the views about human purpose and value expressed in these various Western philosophies. While they make a laudable attempt to be honest and credible, it seems to me that their omission of two major elements of traditional religious belief has deprived them of something essential and hence sacred for the ordering of viable life patterns in human society.

Why Consider "God" and "Soul"?

The first of these major elements of religious belief is that there is a system of reality or power sovereign over men individually and even sovereign over men collectively in any or all human societies—a sovereign system of evolving reality which created man and all other things and upon which man is utterly dependent. Hence man must seek to adapt to the unavoidable requirements for living imposed by that superior system of reality—or else lose life, cease to be.

The second major element of religious belief is a definition of what it is about man and his life that is of long-range importance. Religions characteristically refer to some core element in man's nature which transcends the death of his body.

In Christianity these elements are incorporated in the concepts of "God" and "soul." Such concepts or beliefs are characteristic of non-Judaeo-Christian religions as well. Although the use of the Christian theological terms "God" and "soul" for these two elements of religious belief will raise a number of problems for scholars of theology and religion as well as for scientists and may indeed restrict my meaning, I suggest *god* and *soul* may be used as symbols, providing one does not get uptight about particular meanings, definitions, or characteristic attributes of those terms that one may happen to hold as a result of a particular religious or nonreligious background. In the remainder of this paper I shall italicize *god* and *soul,* using the italics to indicate that these terms are to be symbols that relate in some ways closely to some of their traditional meanings as well as to concepts of the contemporary sciences. I hope readers will hold judgment on exactly what the terms denote until I have more fully shown the new scheme of referents that allow both religious and scientific meanings.

The loss of these religious beliefs about *god* and *soul,* or some moral or psychological equivalent, seriously impairs motivation of long-term purposes or values necessary for man's viability and potential fulfillment. I shall develop later my reasons for saying this and for saying that scientific theory may provide the most powerful support yet available for both these doctrines of the higher religions. But, because the recent humanistic and social philosophies have lacked these essentials, I do not see them as providing a possible way for the future.

It is interesting to note in this connection that there is perhaps as much rebellion within the Communist faith as there is in the West. There are evidences that spiritual restlessness and anomie are growing in all cultures of the world where anthropocentric and limited views of the nature of man have been replacing the traditional religious beliefs.[6] While Plato and Aristotle held significant views on a transcendent power or deity and on an immortality of the *soul,* much of which was incorporated into our Western higher religions, recent social and political philosophies have failed to find credible beliefs of this kind.

On the matter of *soul,* if a man's culture does not provide him with deeply motivating beliefs concerning the not immediately apparent long-range aspects of his own nature, he tends to respond in terms of an untutored, genetically programmed philosophy of "eat, drink, and be merry, for tomorrow you may die." The genetic program is not sufficiently structured to be viable for directing life in a highly complex human society endowed with all the powers provided by the sciences and scientific technologies. Jay Forrester and Dennis Meadows have pointed out that the baffling weakness of the world system of man today is the absence of good knowledge and motivation concerning long-range values. They and their colleagues say they can find no adequate solutions to the problem of maintaining a viable world unless ways are found for engendering suitable long-term values in men.[7] Today man's *soul* seems lost not only in terms of our failure to overcome the private psychological aimlessness and hopelessness felt by sensitive individuals, but also in terms of our failure to integrate men's private purposes with their social purposes. Societies will not function without a culture that informs and motivates its members to purposes extending beyond the interests and lifetimes of its individuals.

On the matter of *god,* if man's culture leads him to belief that makes man the ultimate determiner of his own destiny, then man tends first to feel lost within the morass of human error and perfidy which inevitably characterize his own society, and, second, to feel that his society or even species—and himself with it—is lost. He may have no clear meaning of hope for his existence in the larger scheme of things on which ultimately his experience, if not his religion or his science, is likely to tell him he is dependent. He becomes confused and his morale is especially damaged, if he comes to believe an allegedly undeniable scientific hypothesis that heat death rules out any long-range hope for life, or that he himself is just a freak accident, an absurd joke, that cannot long last in the scheme of things. Scientific views certainly do infect negatively man's hopes, his values, his sense of purpose and meaning—even while he may be denying that scientific facts have anything to do with values. The poignancy of the human situation is manifest in Anthony F. C. Wallace's paper, "Rituals: Sacred and Profane,"[8] which concludes that science defies anyone to believe in *god,* and yet human societies cannot remain in being without such a belief. Wallace and many others who understand the workings of human psyches and societies have sometimes despaired of finding any reasonable way to make a sovereign *god* credible today so that societies can flourish.

I shall therefore seek in this paper to show how belief in a reality sovereign over man (a *god*) and belief in the essential immortality or eternal duration of man's basic nature (a *soul*) not only are necessary for human motivation but are indeed credible on the very grounds of science, which confirms insights common to the higher religious traditions of the world. With recent information revealed by the sciences I think we can provide new grounds for a religious revitalization, one that will provide men with renewed convictions about long-range values or purpose, so that men may not only recover from their spiritual anomie and malaise but also remain viable as a society within the world's ecosystem.

I wish to base my argument on scientific grounds of the highest integrity. I think in the modern sciences we have far surpassed earlier methods by which man finds valid knowledge.[9] However, I have already pointed out that the scientific method does not shun looking into and taking advantage of more ancient accumulations of wisdom, such as the genetic "wisdom of the body"[10] or the traditional wisdom of human cultures.[11] I have already asserted that modern culture has thrown out two essentials for human belief which have been known and prominent in the religions of the world for two or three thousand years at least, some forms of which are necessary for man's understanding of his purpose, meaning, duty, or place in the scheme of things: (1) his utter dependence on a sovereign power transcending man's own powers; and (2) the essentially eternal nature of the core or *soul* of man such that death of the body is not the end of human values and purposes. But before discussing *god* and *soul,* I wish to say something about the problem of human purpose for which I think these concepts are necessary.

Human Purpose and the Role of Religion

It is easy to express the purpose of man in very conventional and well-known language, but that language is almost incredible in the present climate of opinion. I therefore am somewhat hesitant to state it, for I know many will be turned off by the seeming incredibility. But because it persists in representing a reality that I believe contemporary science shows is both valid and necessary, and in order to provide some verbal vision of where this paper will lead, I shall set forth some simple statements about human purpose which are largely common to the traditions of the higher religions of the past two or three thousand years and then proceed to show how many aspects of this picture are corroborated by recent scientific findings of man's place in the scheme of things.

Man's purpose, I suggest, is forever to seek, and to behave in accordance with, the requirements of the sovereign power of the cosmos, of which he is a part, to find ever-higher states of life. Translated into evolutionary theory, the purpose of man is to continue to adapt to the requirements for advancing life laid down by the nature of the cosmic scheme within the local ecosystem he inhabits.

This purpose has been writ in the heart of man by the system of reality which has created him. The purpose has been inscribed in man's genotype, and in the end man cannot successfully resist the purpose of this goal, which is the maintenance and advancement of his ecological niche.[12] Those who do resist will end their line. This same purpose has also been elaborated and inscribed in the culturetypes which inform human societies around the world. But there are periods of radical changes, with the consequent requirement of rapid adaptation, in social as well as biological levels of evolution. This is such a time. Today's cultural information has become inadequate and insufficiently adapted to the radically new habitat of *Homo* produced by radical changes in one portion of human culture: science and technology.

Consequently, in the twentieth century we are in a period of cultural crisis which presents probably the greatest threat to human viability in the past million years. We are presented with the task of adapting the system which we call the human ecological niche to the radical changes brought about by science and technology, as we must if we are to remain a viable species. This task has been imposed by the fact that all cultures and societies of men in the world have been made interdependent by science and technology. It means we must find our new role in a new ecosystem. Moreover, we must do this at the self-conscious, scientifically informed intellectual level since we do not have time for the slower prescientific forms of cultural evolution or the still slower genetic evolution.

Reasonably viable visions of human purpose that provide suitably integrated motivations of psyches and societies have been worked out at semiconscious levels and transmitted in human cultures in the past. In the higher cultures of the world, this purpose was worked out explicitly in the context of their specific societies during the past two or three thousand years by a number of *god*-given geniuses among us, such as Buddha, Confucius, Isaiah, Socrates, Jesus, Muhammad. The task today is to make it explicit for the totally new system of species-wide society structured by a scientific culture. The people of our new one-world society need to know in their hearts the duties and hopes that will enable them to live together with the degree of community that religions provided in the past to the smaller, more or less isolated societies into which the human population was divided.

The necessity for religion stems from the fact that man during the past million years has metamorphized into a new and unique level of life, different in large degree, and hence in kind, from the level of the animal and plant kingdoms. This new level is characterized by the input of the information that sets the norms, goals, and purposes, which shape or structure human behavior patterns, in the form of culturally as well as genetically transmitted memory of what is good. At present, it is quite doubtful that men could survive on the basis of the goals written in their pool of genetic information without additions from the culture's pool of information, even if they were willing to revert to an animal level of behavior.

The more rapid evolution of cultural patterns of information has made possible during the past few thousand years a greater transformation in the nature of living systems on this planet than was made previously over millions of years. This rate of change has been greatly augmented by the rise within cultural evolution of modern science.

This means that we have to prepare for even more rapid changes in the nature of living systems on earth in coming decades. Especially significant and dangerous is the fact that the world has been already made a single community as far as communication and interaction are concerned. Economic goods and military power are deliverable anywhere in short order, and all people's hopes and fears are structured by their vision of what is happening or could happen in distant parts of the world. But the world has not yet been made a single moral community with a sufficiently shared vision of purposes or goals to motivate a sufficiently stable community. If this latter cultural vision does not soon emerge, the world system and the men in it face threats of disruption, disintegration, and decay. When diverse religions are alive and effective within the same socioeconomic system, they tend to generate the kinds of disruptions found in the Mediterranean Basin in the Middle Ages, in Europe during the religious wars, and today in Ireland and Pakistan. When religions are dead or ineffective, the tendency is to a decline of morality and morale, as in the technologically "advanced" populations today. The superposition of a reasonably and effectively integrated religious and moral culturetype on the present common gene pool of the species is a seemingly necessary next step for our viability.

The Source and End of Human Purpose

God is the name for the "absolute and underlying power of the universe," according to one recent authority.[13] In science the search is always on for ever more invariant formulations which explain or predict the manifold events of the universe in terms of the underlying power or forces.

The invariance found in a scientifically established logical or mathematical equation, which can account for an infinite number of changes in the state of a dependent variable according to the various values given by an independent variable, is almost the model to explain what theologians meant in saying that *god*, the absolute and underlying power of the universe, is impassible, omnipotent, immutable, or sovereign. If the equation is irreversible, it is analogous to the theologians' attribution that *god* is that which "molds and fashions the world in the light of ultimate principles or forms" through ever-changing and progressive events toward some ultimate end. The scientific pictures of the second law of thermodynamics and the evolution of states of nature (through successive steps that inhere in the nature of the potential stable states from atoms to molecules, to cells, to organisms, societies, and ecosystems) are examples of the dynamics of cosmic evolutionary trends (including human) presided over by a sovereign reality system whose nature and dynamics can be to some extent revealed or discerned. It would seem that the sciences are revealing more about this process and its universality and interconnectedness than was ever possible before in human history.

I shall not attempt to deal here with the failure of the scientific model of reality to provide an attribute of "person-hood' to *god;* such personhood may not be necessary. In many religions, the ultimate power is not anthropomorphically conceived, and even in the Christian tradition the "three persons" that made up the trinitarian *god* did not identify "person as a self-conscious being as modern usage does."[14] Even the Old Testament or Judaic tradition sought to deanthropomorphize God, whose ways should not be confused with man's ways.[15]

Today, the nature of the sovereign system of reality which created man—and within which and according to which man lives and moves and has his being—has become dim in the minds of men. Many have come to feel that man is master of his own destiny, and they have lost their belief in the practical reality of a transhuman sovereignty. Even theologians have been granting the death of God, and the secular culture has been broadcasting a view, misrepresented as coming from the sciences, that man is in charge of his own destiny, master of his own fate, and king of the world. The recently aroused concern for the ecosystem is a sign that in some degree the scientific information or revelation that there is such a transcendent and sovereign reality is beginning to penetrate public understanding. But this beginning is a long way from an adequate vision of the sovereign power that rules us.

In "Natural Selection and God,"[16] I have tried to make clear that the scientific pictures show man to be as much a product or creature of a transcendent determiner of destiny as ever the religions hypothesized. That man created himself or that he is the prime determiner of his destiny is completely out of keeping with the story of evolution—genetic or cultural—by nature's selection, that is, by the selection of forms that are by nature relatively stable patterns stepped in an indefinitely long

series up a ladder from one level of complexity to another.[17]
And, even in the present state of his powers after a billion years
of evolutionary nursing, man can in no wise do anything unless
he does it in accord with the requirements of the cosmic reality
of which he is part.

For example, man cannot even begin to live without the
energy supplied by the sun and other sources. He cannot fly
without obeying the system of laws that operate in dynamics
and aerodynamics. He is completely dominated by the
requirements imposed by the cosmic system. Man has powers
and "dominates" himself or his habitat only insofar as there is
incorporated within his nature the information of how the
arbitrarily or externally given world system operates and what
it requires of him. Man advances in life only to the degree that
he incorporates the necessary requirements for new levels of
life. Higher human purposes quite transcend man's previous
nature, and man attains them only when he adapts to the
sovereign system of reality within which he lives.

In sum, the scientific picture of man is at least as clear as the
religious traditions that man did not make himself and does not
control his own destiny except insofar as he incarnates the will
or design of the transcendent reality system that did in fact
bring him forth, does sustain him, and destines his future.

There may be a lot of detailed interpretation necessary to
make it clear that the reality system revealed by the sciences is
the same as what the ultimate or sovereign realities pictured by
the traditional religions sought to designate as the gods. Some
of the characteristics and attributes of the traditional gods may
need to be revised if they are to accord with the newer scientific
revelations; but their main features seem to remain significant.
As I said, I shall use the term *god* to denote the total sovereign
system, which in scientific language may be said to be the total
cosmic ecosystem including the details of local ecosystems on
earth.

Though the exercise could be done for many religious traditions, I shall limit myself here to giving some attributes of *god*
that have been presented in the Judaeo-Christian tradition
because members of this symposium and most of our readers
(initially, at least) will be from that tradition, not because I feel
it could not be done for other religious traditions.

Among the main features of traditional attributes or characteristics of *god* as the ultimate reality that determines human
destiny are:

1. *God* is the one and only ultimate reality surrounding and
   infusing man, which created man, and upon which man is
   utterly dependent.
2. *God* has revealed in part *god's* requirements of and *god's*
   disposition to men; hence, *god* is not wholly hidden, alien,
   or mysterious.
3. Yet *god* is in large part hidden, transcendent, beyond what
   man can fully understand—"supernatural"; hence, the
   ultimate mystery of *god*.
4. *God* is lawgiver, the reality or power that determines what
   is right and wrong, and has incarnated or revealed in large
   measure (by a grace sufficient for the day) the requirements
   for good and what is to be avoided as evil in the hearts and
   traditions of creatures.
5. But *god's* continuing program of creation of ever-new
   stages calls upon most evolving creatures to seek the new as
   well as abide by the established requirements that are still
   valid—or else disappear from the scene.
6. The guarantee or justification for the hope of the ultimate
   triumph of *god's* purposes and of all creatures who participate in them, even though any present situation may seem
   to be disastrously short of this triumph, is revealed by a
   careful reading of *god's* mighty acts in the past 6×10^3 years.
7. *God* is gracious to man; that is, without any merit on man's
   part, man has been raised up from the dust and perennially
   sustained and redeemed from his errancy and given the
   opportunity to be a conscious cocreator of *god's* evolving
   Kingdom of Life, as long as man seeks, finds, and executes
   god's requirements.

The characteristics listed here of our creator and sustainer
are not wholly separate, but overlap one another. They may be
listed in other ways, but these ways are helpful for certain
purposes. I shall give more details *seriatim*.

1. I think it self-evident that the first characteristic of deity
or the ultimate reality listed above is recognizably a part of the

scientific picture of the source of man's being. Man is the utterly dependent creature of the transcendent and omnipotent source of flow patterns in the cosmos. The biological term "adaptation" portrays man's historical relation to these characteristics of the superior nature, which has selected the evolving patterns of life from the most primitive to man. Many different sciences have begun to reveal in new detail how man was fashioned literally out of the dust (small particles) or molecules of the earth by the ultimate powers that be. The ecologists are rapidly bringing a generation who have forgotten the supremacy of transcendent reality up against the sharp fact that we cannot in the end violate the ordained requirements and still continue to have life on earth.

The modern sciences go a good deal further than any previous revelations in making clear and valid the hypothesis that *god* is one, or a single system of related parts whose interrelationships in time and space we can increasingly describe in ever-simpler symbols that logically account for ever-larger domains of what we can experience. The sciences make ever clearer that we can never escape from *god's* judgment (selection), even if we flee to the farthest corners of the universe. The different domains of the different sciences are increasingly shown to be different levels of description, describing increasingly interconnectible aspects of our experience of a single system of reality. New areas of science in the past few decades, such as molecular biology and brain studies, are revealing the essential inseparability or oneness of the reality designated by the two domains called "life" and "matter" and the two domains called "mind" and "matter."

Many will be disturbed by the seeming impropriety of my using the term *god* as the totality of the natural world rather than as a being beyond nature, a supernatural being. Without going into great detail, let me say that one can interpret the ancient usage of "supernatural" as referring to a hidden "nature" which is just as "real" as the tangible, visible world "out there" which everyone can see. Hence, "supernatural" means essentially the hidden, subtle forces not immediately obvious to common sense. During the past few centuries the changes in physics have quite obliterated this distinction between nature and supernature. Physicists have themselves become the best revealers of the hidden aspects of the entities and forces not immediately available to common sense, not readily found in what the world presents to the eyes, ears, touch, and other sense receptors. In modern science, "nature" includes the unperceptible ranges of electromagnetic radiations and entities from the invisible and intangible cosmic rays and subatomic particles to the great generalizations such as the laws of thermodynamics. The new "nature" of physics includes and describes the invisible "spirits" that animate men and shape men's "visions"—describes them as "natural" and "material" entities such as complex patterns of molecular structures and behaviors. These supersensory and supercommonsense entities commonly dealt with by contemporary science as "nature" are precisely the kinds of things that earlier usage meant by "supernatural." Hence, the sovereign system presiding over the world and human destiny described by the sciences is properly "supernatural" if the word is used in its former meaning, and is properly "natural" if the word is used in the sense now common among scientists. I do not recall that even the "linguistic" theologians have straightened out this problem of the meaning of "supernatural." Since for most scientists the natural universe includes all that really is, it includes all that was real for the earlier theologians who may have used the word "supernatural" to refer to some special class of reality that was not "naturally" observable. For many scientists there is commonly no meaning left for the term "supernatural" since for them all reality is classed as "natural"—even the still hidden and unknown characteristics of the cosmos.

2. The revelation to or the incarnation in man of information about the nature and requirements of the ultimate and sovereign reality which created man is a patent fact of genetic and cultural evolution. At every stage of evolving life, so scientists suppose, the surrounding reality has selected and presented to each new generation the information of the essential requirements that this reality ordains for living systems. The genotype is the scientific name for revelation at one level; it is literally incarnated within man in the DNA molecular alphabet. The culturetype or socially transmitted wisdom is the name for revelation at another level of scientific analysis of

human life; and it is widely believed that this is also incarnated in the central nervous system by transmissions of information that are received both with and without conscious awareness, and which, along with the already incarnated genotypic information, shapes the molecular structures of the brain and hence the feelings, thoughts, and behaviors of men in such ways that men respond to the environment as a living system. Within the evolution of cultures, it seems clear that all populations are indebted to the critically significant revelations (about man and his relation to *god*) that have been made in the past by men who are sometimes symbolized as the *god*-sent saviors.

3. The third characteristic of *god* is clear, especially to those at the forefront of the sciences, namely, that we do not and probably even cannot know or fully prove the ultimate nature of reality. Much of contemporary philosophy of science, as well as the logic of the Gödel theorem, suggests why. While man has been given much useful knowledge, through what has been selected in his genetic and cultural heritage, the creative process and its creations ever remain a wonderful mystery for further exploration. While we sometimes feel bound by our finite capacity for counting to speak of a beginning and an ending, an alpha and an omega, this is only a symbol of the finitude of our brains and not necessarily a proper model of the reality we contemplate. The scientific theories of the cosmos, like their earlier predecessors in religious cosmic poetry, present the possible logical alternatives of either a finite or an infinite series in space and time. Likewise, while the scientific community is proud that it knows something about the world, its pioneers, at least, are certain that what now seems quite reasonable and true may tomorrow become a discarded theory or paradigm.[18] "Reality" is not necessarily fully symbolized in what men happen to think or feel about it. In the evolution of our understanding, as well as in the evolution of prehuman information about how to live, we must forever adapt ourselves to the new and extended conditions of reality presented to us.

4. The fourth attribute of *god* stems from the first three and states how the omnipotent whole, (1) of which man is a part and which created man and sustains him, (2) whose law for having life is partially inscribed in man's heart, and (3) whose

further requirements we must continue to seek, all adds up to (4) providing man with a "divine" or "cosmic" purpose—a goal or aim implied in the evolving character of the life system in which we participate. The laws or norms of life (selected and sustained by the nature of the total reality of the larger ecosystem—including at least the solar system—and inscribed in DNA and in culture) were given us as a heritage of unearned grace, which has defined the purposes of our lives. Like the sparrows and the lilies, we have goals and norms which we delight in carrying out and which yield the rich complexities of our lives. We like to breathe, to eat and drink, to keep suitably warm or cool, to procreate, and to do most of the other things that the sovereign creator of life requires for the maintenance and advancement of living systems. This is a sort of Garden of Eden picture before we consider the problem of our continuing consciously—after eating of the fruit of the Tree of Knowledge that makes us aware of the future—to adapt to the new requirements for the further building or evolving of the life system.

5. The fifth attribute of *god* is the continuing program of creation of life to raise it to ever-higher levels of complexity and wonder. It is here that man, already endowed by grace with a complex system of tried and tested norms, aims, goals, or purposes that yield life, must now adventure beyond the already known and revealed into discovering new patterns of life adapted to future requirements. In the advanced stages of human culture, after man began eating from the Tree of Knowledge, cultural evolution of *god's* kingdom of life began, and man was called to participate in it consciously.

Hence, a prime purpose of man is to risk himself and some suffering in serving to help build *god's* future Kingdom of Life. This is a new level of purpose, a higher order of purpose which is a program for seeking new norms, aims, or goals required for a higher, more complex level of life. It is only as man participates on the exploratory and developing edge of evolving life systems that he has to unlearn or revise inherited information and search for better patterns of living. When man is at the edge—beyond the protective and nourishing circle of the already established grace that *god* has provided up to the point where man's phenotypic living starts— he has the necessity to question, not *god's* goodness or power, but man's own completeness. Both theology and science explain man's perennial incompleteness.

At this point, if man wishes to continue in the forefront of building *god's* Kingdom of Life on earth, he must let perish or die the inadequate elements of his prior-existing state and reform or replace them by entering on a further search for states acceptable to *god's* coming Kingdom or purpose. This is by ordination a path of suffering and confusion (symbolized by the way of the cross) for the body or phenotype and for the associated perceptions of self and world provided by the brain. It will mean the death of certain of the present patterns of the organized system of the brain or body. Sooner or later it requires a discarding of the existing phenotype altogether.This is the way our creator has ordained that we evolve to our present stage of life, and there do not appear to be any alternatives but continual struggle with suffering and death of the phenotype forever in the future.

This would be a rather bleak and hopeless view if we did not have an insight into the immortal or eternal nature of the human *soul* and the potential joy and triumph of man, even on the cross, even in renouncing all his worldly goods and pleasures, even in the midst of the nastiest and otherwise most discouraging circumstances. Because the present phenotype is only a transient part of the full system or nature we call man, I shall later introduce a scientifically based doctrine of man's larger nature or *soul* that transcends death and defeat, since upon such a notion we are dependent for psychological and social viability in the world.

6. The sixth characteristic of the sovereign power in our cosmos, the surety that *god* will ultimately triumph over all evil and that his Kingdom will grow and prevail forever, implies that if we are to remain as partners in bringing about the Kingdom, we then can be sure that our *souls* shall live and that our purposes shall prevail and triumph over death and evil. While I shall deal with the reality of our *soul's* participation later, I shall indicate here something of the scientific evidence for the ultimate triumph of the Kingdom of the sovereign

power. It is essentially one of those scientific truisms that are
tautological: If there is a scheme or system of things that is in
fact inevitably moving in some direction, then it certainly will
move in that direction. The increase of entropy in time is such a
statement. We make this kind of tautological statement meaningful in history insofar as we are able to point to and empirically confirm real trends that actually take place according to
such a law. We can and do find formulas or models of the
reality system that enable our prophecy or prediction of events
in ways which then are confirmed or validated in experience.

Our scientific expansion of the history of our evolution to
more than a billion years ago is such a basis for understanding
that things are happening in some orderly program or process
of development that accounts for a certain direction thus far.
Our discernment of evolution's laws or modes of operation
offers some perspective on the future. It is important to note
some recent developments that say something about the general overall trends of this evolutionary history. Today we have
a much longer history and in much more detail than was
available when the cosmologies of traditional religions were
created.

Within the nineteenth century the scientists extended our
historical perspective from a few thousand to a few million
years, and within the past few decades they have revealed
much about another thousandfold extension of our time span.
They have given evidence of the creation of life from the dust
of the cosmos and have detailed something of how it has been
done. One of the findings has been that life has been evolving
in a direction from disorder to order, from chaos and void to
form. This trend from chaos to order is not a new observation
or hypothesis; but it is now given in much greater detail, with
more grounds for credibility, and for a much longer time span.
Both Erwin Schrödinger and Norbert Wiener noted this
movement of life in a direction they called negentropic.[19] Yet
they and most other good scientists also noted that a very
plausible interpretation of the second law of thermodynamics
spells the doom of life and order in the end. This has raised a
difficult problem for understanding the purpose of human life.

There has been in the past two decades a good deal of effort
to understand why life *seems* to be running counter to this basic

physical law. The most general interpretation of the second law by scientists for the past century is made with the assumption that the universe is a closed system and that increased entropy and the death of all further life by the eventual exhaustion of available energy is inevitable. One of the most significant breakthroughs to a better physical interpretation and a better ground for theological interpretation in my opinion has been that of J. Bronowski, who pointed out that while the second law of thermodynamics "is a *true theorem in combinatorial arithmetic,* and (like other statistical laws) *a fair guess at the behavior of long runs* . . . it tells us little about the natural world which, in the years since the Second Law seemed exciting, has turned out to be full of preferred configurations and hidden stabilities, even at the most basic and inanimate level of atomic structure."[20]

In Bronowski's interpretation, as for biological theory in general, the movement of evolution is determined by processes of small steps. But his interpretation suggests that each step to a new level is a step provided by random fluctuations around an existing norm, some of which fluctuations are bound to hit upon new hidden stabilities or preferred configurations that are characteristics inherent in the universe. In some respects, Bronowski's theory is similar to that of Herbert Simon and that of Ross Ashby,[21] where evolution of complexity takes place as the result of random variations in level A finding stable or preferred states at a new level B within the limits of a narrow spread of variability. Then variations around step B produce the discovery of a new level, C, and so on up a ladder of stable states that are intrinsic to the nature of the various levels of the hierarchies of evolving systems. If the universe were indeed a closed system, evolution toward successively higher levels of complexity by random variations discovering stable niches would be doomed eventually to cease further evolving by the second law of thermodynamics, for eventually the supply of energy to generate variations to achieve higher levels of complexity would become exhausted. This cosmology might give us a frozen heaven of some final perfection of complex forms never to be disrupted because all the available energy of the closed-system cosmos will have been exhausted.

But we do not have any way to prove the ultimate character

of the cosmos. What is significant is that the character of the cosmos does provide grounds for discerning the direction of evolution, for that frontier of events in time which represents the penetration to ever-new states of realization of the hidden preferences intrinsic to the nature of the cosmos or *god*. As far as man is concerned, this can continue for as long a time in the future as in the past under our present cosmologies. The period of time is at least as long as our information about events in it is secure. For all practical purposes, this is indefinitely long. And hence man today, even with the present high levels of scientific information, must remain as unsure about *god's* ultimates as are some theologians.[22] If we postulate our plans on what to do for a million or a billion years, we shall have enough to keep us busy. What is important is our knowledge that there is a direction in time, a purpose, pointing to goals to be attained in the future. The scientific reality of cosmic evolution and its direction is more certain than the hypotheses about ultimate parameters, whether of finite or infinite character. *God's* kingdom is a kingdom of development, evolution, or process—not merely random motions in a static frame. About the ultimate nature of *god,* or the total reality, we probably will remain uncertain, and we can say "sufficient unto the next millennium are the problems thereof."

Most scientific cosmologies or world systems indicate the essentially inevitable or predestined motion from one level to another in evolution according to nature's intrinsic, hidden preference. If we cast our lot to continue working for *god's* kingdom thus defined, we are bound to triumph with it. If we wish to opt out, we shall merely cease to be. Trust in *god* we must.

This *god* which is utterly transcendent, impassible, and triumphant, seems to imply little significance or room for man's independent efforts in the larger cosmos of *god* or nature. In prescientific language it poses the question of whether man has any freedom or power of his own, any responsibilities at all, or whether he is a puppet. It raises a host of other questions about man's relation to the creator and operator of the cosmic process within which we live and move and have our being.

7. This brings us to the seventh attribute or characteristic I have ascribed to the nature of the ultimate ecosystem: *god's*

essential "graciousness." I am here referring to the important element of Christian thought called "grace." Other religions have different ways and terms for allowing man to have hope for his future in spite of his present inadequacies (sin) and wretchedness. I shall not here enter into the varying views of *god's* grace within Christendom, nor attempt evaluation of their relative validity, nor seek to compare their validity with related views in other religions. I shall simply seek to show how this rather important religious function—to provide men with salvation in spite of their errors and misery—can be ascribed to the sovereign nature revealed by the sciences. In this task I shall confine myself to the Judaeo-Christian views.

The scientific pictures, it seems to me, support the biblical view that man is an image or reflection of the cosmic reality which created him, and man has been made one with it, a partner or steward in the program of bringing about the kingdom of advancing life.

Man, in the scientific picture, is seen as especially endowed with powers to carry on the work of *god's* program of evolving—we may say, of evolving toward higher levels of complexity of life in a direction roughly implied by evolution thus far from molecules to man. Human endowments for this task are especially manifest in cultural evolution. Instead of *god's* power overwhelming man and making no place for man's efforts in the scheme of things, it seems that *god's* selection of a creature capable of cultural evolution has endowed man with special powers and freedom to discover new levels of hidden preferences in the scheme of things. In this man is the most highly endowed creature on earth for the most rapid further evolutionary development.

The scientific picture helps us with the old theological problem of theodicy, the problem of a good and omnipotent *god* as creator of evil in the world. This is related to the old query of whether there was also an evil *god* or devil, and the related ancient debate as to whether sinners might be damned forever.

The answer I read from the scientific revelations (literally, unveilings) is that there is no eternal hell. The living systems that fail to meet the requirements for survival simply cease to be. Patterns that do not exist can hardly experience suffering. The patterns that survive and evolve to more complex levels are all that count in any measurement of progress in that direction. The other patterns simply are unstable and disappear from the ecosystem. Each error, each random mutation that does not discover a new level of stability, is erased and a new opportunity to try again is provided to all that remains in being. Suffering is reserved for the righteous or living.

It is true that living men and animals fear, and rightly so, being caught in the forces that destroy life. This fear, however, is a good, for purposes of remaining alive, in that it enables the living to move from evil toward good, from destruction and death to life. The movement toward the good and away from the evil is the source of hope, joy, and pleasure, just as the movement toward evil is the source of the fears and pains that warn against evil and death and thus provide man with his capacity to distinguish good from evil. These homeostatic mechanisms have already been selected and abound in a hierarchy throughout all levels of living systems as a grace already granted. But, since they are homeostatic, negative-feedback mechanisms, the neurological patterns (and corre-lated consciously experienced patterns) are "symbols" or mod-els of the reality system. These models disappear when the lethal event—which is ultimate judgment—hits the living sys-tem. The living system and the self-guiding purposes or models it produces by neural configurations disappear when the system disintegrates. At least this is my understanding of what most scientists dealing with these phenomena believe. In such a system there is no eternal hell.

It is only for the living that there can be joy and fear, and in the living the *selected* mechanisms that produce joy and fear are balanced in such a way that life tends to be a desired and sometimes exciting venture toward the building of a kingdom of a more complex hierarchy or ecosystem, whose ultimate triumph as far in the future as we can project is assured by the ultimate nature and power of the almighty cosmic sovereignty evolving in time.

As in all theological inquiries, the questions about the nature of *god* lead to questions about the nature of man, and back to *god,* and forth to man. It is, in the history of ideas, the same dialogue that has been going on between genotype and habitat to find ever-more complex and stable phenotypes or ecological niches. We have been moving into the question of the nature of man, and I have suggested that it becomes essential for human culture to correct a natural error about man's real nature that now needs correcting. We have misread the death of the body as the death of the real self.

Without a mutation that destroys the old pattern and makes a new one, there is no new life. Without a change in the habitat that forces the destruction of some values of a former species, there is no new ecological niche for the new species at a higher level of development. Since man's place or purpose in *god's* kingdom has been historically one as a pioneer on the expanding exploration toward ever-more complex forms able to remain stable in ever-wider ranges of the solar system's habitat, and since functioning as an element of this frontier requires continual death of former stages and continual emergence in new patterns, in both genetic and cultural stages, man will fail if in his cultural mechanisms he does not establish suitable "desires" for death and transfiguration of the more transient elements of his nature. In this requirement of the evolutionary process, cultural mechanisms must do as genetic mechanisms have done. It is for this reason that we must turn to a doctrine of the human *soul,* a doctrine of man's reality which transcends the coming and going of phenotypes, of waking and sleeping, and other more transient states.

Animal genotypes automatically grace animal behaviors with suitable hope and courage so that each animal will fight for life—and especially the life of the species—in the midst of conditions that to many human observers seem hopeless for them as individual creatures. But one cannot conceive how a genotype could be evolved to protect man from the dismay and fears that have come to him as a result of the joint evolution of forebrain and cultural memories to perceive the inevitable end or death of the bodily or phenotypic life that he, because of his genetic heritage, naturally cherishes. Dobzhansky and many others have pointed to the awareness of death as the source of that universal cultural phenomenon we know as religion.[23] Eating of the fruit of the tree of knowledge of good and evil, and thus coming to see an evil against which his naïve or genetically informed wisdom could not protect him, man is *now* destined to wrestle *consciously* with the problem of overcoming evil with good. Hence man must become dependent on cultural information in addition to that in his genotype. But, in order to do this, it becomes clear that his culture must overcome the hope-killing conclusions that disrupt his consciousness and undermine his motivation, conclusions to which he logically comes when he has been led to suppose that his ultimate and only significant nature is snuffed out with the death of his body.

What is Man?

For understanding human purpose not only do we need a doctrine of the scheme of things that ultimately determines human destiny, but also we need to understand man as an element of that system. Again, the view I am going to refer to is somewhat preposterous to contemporary culture. Yet I believe that when properly translated it has basic validity, confirmed by the most recent scientific views.

This view is, in a most important aspect, equivalent to the doctrine that some of the great religions have called "soul" or "spirit." These terms denote an invisible something that animates and shapes man, the source of his will (purpose) and reason (his concious decision making). The term *soul* was used to designate the true or ultimate nature of the self, something that is in an important way different from the body in that it does not die with the body or, if it does die, it nevertheless is typically resurrected, reincarnated, or somehow continued so that it may progress (over generations, or as far as man's present awareness of himself is concerned, even instantly) to become fully redeemed. "Redemption," or equivalent terms of various cultures, implies justified, comforted, and significantly integrated and at peace with the sovereign eternal whole of reality. The *soul,* as a model or picture of some invisible reality central to man's nature which may continue after the death of the body, is an ancient belief which is largely dismissed in recent, secular culture and also even in religious cultures, where its traditional conceptualization has become incredible because of failure to interpret it in the light of new knowledge.

"Soul" is not a concept used in the Judaic source of Christianity but comes from Greek philosophy, perhaps from Far

Eastern notions, perhaps from Egypt. It was worked into
Christian doctrine by the early Christian theologians, largely
after the New Testament was written, in order to adapt Christ-
ianinty to the reigning "science" or "philosophy" of the
Mediterranean world of that time—Neoplatonism. The immortality of the *soul*—as the core seat of human will and reason
which could continue after the body died—became the successor to the Judaic and biblical view held by the earliest Christ-
ians that salvation would come about by means of the resurrection of the dead.

Today, neither of these traditions is credible in any literal
way in terms of twentieth-century secular and scientific ways of
viewing man and the world. I shall not here go into the long
history of these different views or models for ultimate salvation
in Christian theology, oscillating between the advantages and
disadvantages of the models of the disembodied soul and the
resurrection of the body, like the oscillation in physical theory
between light as waves or particles. The important point is that
there have been models or theories of how to understand and
to motivate men concerning the continuity of basic human
values beyond the death of the body, models which have been
more or less credible and helpful in the history of human
societies to motivate men or provide them with purposes, aims,
and goals which cannot possibly be achieved during the lifetime
of any individual body or phenotype. As I have said, I have
chosen to use the term *soul* in this paper to symbolize any
model which serves this purpose, including the resurrection of
the body.

Our present historical crises and our anthropology, psychology, and biology suggest that some equivalently effective view
of how some real core of human nature survives death is
essential for understanding human purpose and meaning and
that this view is necessary for meaningful hope and capacity to
survive, at least for persons who eat enough from the tree of
knowledge and who reflect deeply on man's nature. For many
people still, of course, the genetically given grounds for hope
and duty provide implicitly for man's motivation (aims, goals,
purposes) to do many of those things he must do for the future
of this *soul* after the death of his body. But the more aware
man becomes of the complex elements of his role in the life

system presented by the sciences and the more he becomes aware that uncultivated notions of who he is do not adequately fit in this new view, then the more he needs to be correctly informed about his true being, or *soul*.

The reality of the core nature of a man, as an unseen something that transcends the life of the body, is, of course, quite common in contemporary science. The sciences are daily revealing new aspects of such elements of this invisible reality as the genotype and the culturetype, both of which program the neurophysiological patterns that activate behavior and consciousness. Behavior and consciousness are shaped by the interactions of genotype and culturetype with the transcultural habitat, which we could similarly call "cosmotype." What makes the religious concepts of *soul* incredible today is not that what religion seeks to symbolize is essentially untrue, but that our religious culture has failed to translate from the ancient conceptual schemes that used to be the grounds for terms such as "soul," "breath," "spirit," "reincarnation," "resurrection," or "immortality" into the conceptual schemes of contemporary science.

Certainly one can say that the enduring primary patterns of bodily and behavioral phenotypes—based upon information recorded in the gene pool and cultural pool and statistically shuffled—are in fact reincarnated (surrounded by a new set of amino acids) or resurrected (rise again from zygotes into new creatures or phenotypes). This occurs for genotypes even of those phenotypes producing no direct children, since essentially all of the statistically significant elements of the genotype of the sterile phenotype are widely shared in the gene pool. Certain patterns of information in the human gene pool have been continuous for millions, even hundreds of millions, of years. Moreover, recent scientific views suppose there is continuity with the earlier billions of years of evolution from atoms through complex chemicals to primitive living systems. This gives an enduring reality in the past to a *soul* or core reality of human nature.[24]

Similar views are held concerning the continuity of human cultures over the millennia of evolution of languages, technologies, religions, and other culturally transmitted patterns.[25]

However, when in 1951 I presented a paper on the *soul* to

the third meeting of the Society for the Scientific Study of Religion, in which I outlined a scientifically based "trinitarian" doctrine of the human *soul*—similar to the one I am presenting here, involving "cosmotype" (habitat), "genotype," and "culturetype"—not many seemed to understand that I was talking about something either real or relevant. This picture of the long-range core of human nature leaves most people cold since the older models of *soul* do not stand up very well and since people are not yet sufficiently familiar with the new models (which may be real enough scientifically) to cathect either type of model with their motivational system or "gut" feelings.

The patterns of human attention and concern or consciousness evolve. Their primary information (that which shapes them) is programmed by the genotype, which induces basic bodily homeostatic mechanisms (goals or purposes) necessary for maintaining, transmitting, and evolving life.[26] But just as children must be programmed or induced by nongenotypic information to speak languages and operate technologies—so as to avoid touching bare electric wires and charged third rails, for instance—so must men generally be informed by culture concerning the necessities or realities of a complex culturally structured life.[27]

The genotypic programming of animals has been selected to provide behavior that brings about the death of the body in good time and without making the creatures who do it morbid about it. The programming of death is a necessity for evolution. Knowledge that permits contemplation of death is neither necessary nor does it seem possible for animals before man. Dobzhansky and others, as I have said, have noted that human religions were born among men when they first became aware of death and began to wonder about their own future when their bodies would die. Ancient religions, or newer ones, have long assured us that death is not the end. Certainly bodies die. But today the sciences present a model about life that is equivalent in meaning to religious views of *soul*. The real core of human nature is not any particular body but an enduring pattern of flow.[28] The flow pattern is generated by the interaction of the energy and boundary conditions set by habitat (or cosmotype), genotype, and culturetype, resulting in unending successions of ever-evolving levels of living forms. Culturally transmitted information may be cathected with genetically derived somatic structures to orient human behavior to those longer-range goals of life embodied in the soul.

Unless man can transcend the inhibiting and alienating fears that he has no meaning or purpose beyond his present or prospective bodily condition, his private psychological hopes and motivations tend to become disrupted; hence he will tend *not* to risk himself for society's goals that lie beyond his personally felt interests.

But as a sociocultural animal man is not viable unless he is motivated to long-term social goals. Jay Forrester[29] has pointed out that the critical problem for the future of the world system is the adequate cultural regeneration of man's long-range values and that this is the traditional function of religion. Society cannot survive without enculturating such values or purposes. The purposes or goals ascribed to the *soul* thus provide linkages between the purposes of individual bodies and the long-range purposes of society, of the species, and ultimately of the cosmic ecosystem.

Before the purposes of the long-range core of man's being can be made real to either children or wise men in the context of scientific models of reality, it must be a credible model within that realm of ideas which are accepted as valid. The fact that men may go so far beyond what is normally credible in order to harbor some vision of their worth in the scheme of things is a temporary necessity which grace often has provided genotypically; but this is not ultimately sufficient. Man must therefore find reasonable, rationally credible grounds for hope. The scientific views of man today can provide that ground. But for general social use it will need to be developed into a credible and rationally articulated conceptual system that checks in with scientific beliefs generally. This conceptual system must also be cathected to man's affective system, tied to the gentically structured systems of the brain that produce what we know as aesthetic and libidinal feelings which motivate human attitudes and behavior. For communication to all stages and ages of men all this will need to be clothed by poets, and dramatists, and other creative artists in language and art forms suitable to convey meaning at the various levels necessary for satisfying the various requirements of understanding and feeling found in human populations. First, however, the theologian, like the scientist, needs to express in the clearest, most rational possible scientific idiom the reality of a concept of *soul;* otherwise his words will not be able to communicate—with *credibility* among the cultural leaders who accept the scientific world view—the subtle and hidden realities of man, his *god,* and his salvation. Such communication is probably now necessary for the viability of societies in a modern scientific setting.

One of the reasons why my trinitarian doctrine of man's *soul* seems cold is that it is stochastic, or composed of separate states that relate to one another as statistical variables. Observations of individual events do not yield meaningful patterns until a sufficient number are perceived as an ensemble. The individual human genotype is a unique form of a statistical variable sampled from the gene pool of *Homo.* Likewise, the individual culturetype inscribed in the central nervous system of any particular man is a statistical sample from the pool of his culture. Similarly, an individual's history of development in his particular habitat is a product of statistical samples of the variations of man's world. The combination of these three statistical samples in any single life or phenotype is itself a very unique sample. The different phenotypes, or any short-time sections of a phenotype, are thus statistical concretions of unique and discrete elements, none of which will exist in the future in exactly the same pattern. The same, of course, is true for all events in the cosmos. The molecules of a gas never are the same identical pattern. As the Greek philosopher Heraclitus noted, one can never step into the same river twice. Yet we commonly call the river the same and suppose that something real and essentially the same is there all the time. We have to do a similar thing in talking about a human *soul,* which, like the river, is from a certain perspective a more useful image of an important reality than the varying particles that constitute it.

The true nature of man in the long run is not the unique phenotype of the moment, but the underlying patterns of the boundary conditions that determine the flow. They have a long. essentially eternal history relative to the transient, stochastic states that constitute them. A man's *soul,* like a river, not only is the water molecules now in it, but it is the shape of the bed of the river and the persisting flow patterns of the water. We have to look outside and inside and beyond the elements of our phenotype to our role in the continuing evolution of mankind and life systems if we are to see our *soul*. It is and has been the business of religions to formulate this kind of vision of *soul* in ways to be acceptable to individual minds within their particular cultures, so that men can see their true significance and so they will not be deluded by what is transient and of less significance.

Biology reveals how various recombinations of genotypes in a gene pool and their successive reincarnations or resurrections in a stream of phenotypes constitute the picture of the statistical variables that generate the ascending flow of animal and plant behavior in an eternal upward-climbing stream that represents a more significant picture of realities than the particularities of a phenotype. But contemporary religions have failed to bring their doctrines of the death-transcending reality of man up to date. I am suggesting that the sciences today offer much more credible and even "material" evidences of the *soul* than the religions of the past were able to do. I suggest that in the future, by a new vision of the reality of *soul,* men's behavior can be much more effectively motivated to longer-range and more significant values than is now the case.

The motivational system established in prehuman animals by the genotype had no problem with the long-range values of the species beyond the death of the individual body, as I have already pointed out. Since all cultural modifications of human patterns of living are ultimately grounded in the genetic patterns, there should be in principle no problem in culturally induced motivation to serve the longer-range purposes of the *soul* as well as the purposes of its temporary phenotypic expressions. The present nature of the information in the human gene pool, which has been evolving symbiotically in viable ways for a half-million years with the complex overlays of culturetype, encourages our belief in this potential, as does also the theory that nature will continue to weed out the unstable and favor the stable or "preferred" patterns of complex dynamic flows in the future.

However, there is a double danger that the present badly

informed cultural patterns concerning the soul's long-range values will bring about great damage not only to the cultures and the societies they inform, but even to the gene pool that permitted them. This latter is even more sacred. Prior to the late twentieth century, semi-isolated segments of culturetypes and genotypes were pruned by disasters brought about by bad culturetypes, thus selecting the more viable patterns of religious enculturation. Today, however, since there is no longer any isolation and little semi-isolation of subunits of *Homo,* there is no place for a subspecies genetically or culturally to develop independently and thus provide the possibility for selection of one variant as a variable pattern that might survive in case the others go on a path of self-destruction. It is therefore urgent, if self-conscious, rational man wishes to avoid a serious evolutionary setback here on earth, he must recognize that the long-range values of the human *soul* be revitalized as quickly as possible and that the brotherhood of man under a common, sovereign, transhuman aegis be reestablished.

From the general theory of evolving systems of patterns of flow, including life, we can conclude with a good deal of confidence that those patterns which have long-range stability are another way of saying nature has selected and will select them. We can conclude about the boundary conditions and dynamic flow patterns that structure man—including the habitat, gene pool, and culturetypes—that human phenotypes and social patterns will in the end meet these requirements for long-range stability. Those variants that do not will perish, like the wicked in the biblical literature. Those that do meet these requirements will flourish, like the righteous. Since the long-range patterns of stability are not seen in the phenotype apart from the structures that persist to give long-range stability to the species, we have to look to these long-range structures to understand the true nature of man.

Conclusion

I have suggested that I have been translating into scientific language what religions, and Platonic philosophy in particular, have called *soul.* I have pointed to the fact that, since selection of genotypes and culturetypes must in fact provide for the long-range values of the living system or else disappear from the scene, there should be no hesitancy in expecting a revitalization of man's belief in the reality of his long-range nature, symbolized as *soul,* and of his motivation to serve it even more faithfully than he is motivated to serve his body, just as for a half-billion years our ancestors have been selected to serve the species as a higher priority motivation than mere self-preservation.

George Wald has delighted in telling of the male of the insect species, the praying mantis, who continues copulating to insure the future of his species even while his female partner continues to devour him from the head toward the rear. One might say the male had lost his head not only metaphorically, but also literally. In fact, however, this genetically programmed self- or phenotype-sacrificing behavior of the male is wiser for the vitality or life of the species than what even human heads can ordinarily figure out. Evidence from social insects provides abundant reasons for concluding that genetically motivated preference for self-sacrifice of the body for the *soul,* including for its social functions, not only is possible but is the order of the day.

In man, self-sacrifice for others is not genetically programmed in a direct way, as it is in the social insects.[30] But man has overcome this by socially programming the enculturation of certain informational patterns within the central nervous systems of individuals. By such enculturations men may, and sometimes do, transcend the social insects by building on genetic information in much more complex ways. With men there is much wider freedom to each individual within more complex social systems. Yet human self-sacrifice also can reach the point of the heroism of the kamikaze or the man who lays down his life, not only for his brother or family, but for a much larger society. History and anthropology show that such service to long-range values of society and species has been and can be induced among humans by suitable reinforcement programs, which usually include at least a modicum of rationally credible myth or philosophy. This has been the function of religious institutions, which in the world today are in some cases nearly bankrupt or impotent because their power to create a credible myth has been eroded by their failure to adapt their myths or beliefs to accord with what is credible in the scientific world view.

I suggest that a new doctrine of *soul* or man's death-transcending reality will so adequately fit in with the basic realities of the human gene pool, and also fit the environmental (including cultural) demands for human responsiveness to the long-range values required for continued advancement of life, that such a revision of the cultural pattern of the religious doctrine of *soul* will be very likely. I suggest further that this enlarged vision of who man is will make possible man's entry into the complex new level of cultural evolution entailed by science and technology. Without such a new doctrine, I am inclined to be as pessimistic as the Club of Rome investigators and despairing poets, novelists, and dramatists, but for many more reasons (psychological, biological, cosmological, or theological as well as sociological) than those to which they point.

I have already pointed out that man's understanding of *god's* grace—or of the relevance and purpose of man in the scheme of things—is not understandable apart from a new vision by man of who he himself is. And this requires that he envision his eternal *soul,* for in terms of his reasonable expectations for his phenotype alone he cannot win—and life would be indeed absurd. But, with his heart and eye set upon the values of his *soul,* he can make sense of *god's* objective requirements, and he can see a truly significant and hopeful place for himself in the scheme of things. For those in the Christian tradition this means they can find that *god* (symbolizing the sovereign source of all things and events) may be understood as fully good and gracious without this conflicting with his being the source of evil and death—provided we understand that evil and death are names of what the *soul* overcomes in fulfilling its purpose in an everlasting search and achievement of ever-higher adaptations of life. This search-and-achievement is a new synonym for the triumphal advance of the Kingdom of God.

In scientific language, a concept of man's death-transcending nature is thus necessary to provide the proper understandings and feelings to motivate him to the long-range purposes, goals, or trends ordained for his evolution by the ultimate system that selects or determines destiny. A recognition of the nature of that system is the other major doctrine that needs to enter man's enculturation. These two requirements are essentially the same as a religious revitalization of the symbols called *soul* and *god*, if man is to be saved from his own foolish pride in trivial elements of a transient phenotypic expression—a pride that could lead to extinction of the species. These two major religious doctrines and the scientific information to back them up are, then, a most significant *purpose* for one who would help save mankind as well as his own *soul* from present trends toward self-destruction.

Coda

I have here passed by many important intellectual problems that will need to be covered before we can fully resolve the various intellectual problems that men may have with this major thesis of human purpose in terms of scientific doctrines of *god* and *soul*. But I trust that this may be enough to start us on our way. I think we can resolve the major questions that people may have about the personhood or anthropocentric models of *god* as easily as about *god's* "supernatural" character, about the problem of freedom in a world fully controlled by *god*, about the threats of scientific doctrines of a cosmos that at first sight seem ultimately hostile to man, and about the grounds of knowledge (epistemology, revelation, scientific method). I have pointed to some answers to these problems in this and other papers, and I hope to provide more detail later. But for now I think it most important to show that two of the most unlikely of traditional religious notions in the present secular climate of opinion—a transcendent and omnipotent *god*, and man's immortal *soul*—are most essential for understanding human purpose and human salvation, and are readily interpretable as valid and essential in the light of contemporary scientific knowledge.

NOTES

1. Donella H. Meadows et al., *The Limits to Growth: A Report for the Club of Rome's Project on the Predicament of Mankind* (New York: Universe Books, 1972).

2. See Theodore Roszak, *The Making of a Counter Culture* (New York: Doubleday & Co., 1969); and *Where the Wasteland Ends: Politics and Transcendence in Post-industrial Society* (New York: Doubleday & Co., 1972); Charles A. Reich, *The Greening of America: How the Youth Revolution Is Trying to Make America Livable* (New York: Random House, 1970); T. S. Eliot, *The Waste Land and Other Poems* (1922; New York: Harcourt Brace & Co., 1955); Aldous Huxley, *Brave New World* (New York: Harper & Row, 1932); George Orwell, *1984* (New York; Harcourt Brace & Co., 1949); Dorothy Martin, *No Place to Hide* (Chicago: Moody Press, 1971).

3. Roszak, *Making of a Counter Culture* and *Where the Wasteland Ends*.

4. Arnold Toynbee, *An Historian's Approach to Religion* (New York: Oxford University Press, 1956), esp. chap. 13.

5. Robert N. Bellah, in his "Civil Religion in America" (*Daedalus* [Winter 1967], pp. 1-21), has suggested how a kind of national cultus has come to replace traditional religion here. Clyde Kluckhohn ("The Scientific Study of Values and Contemporary Civilization," *Zygon* 1 [1966]: 230-43) is representative of many social scientists who view the Marxist salvation program and those of nazism, fascism, and many other older and newer social, philosophic, psychologic, and other cults as having a religious character—for better or worse.

6. For similar problems in another ancient religion, see Isma'īl R. al Fārūqī, "Science and Traditional Values in Islamic Society," *Zygon* 2 (1967): 231-46. In the past decade, the *New York Times* and other papers and journals have carried many dozens of news stories and magazine articles on the restlessness and spiritual rebellion of youth in many countries. This is reflected in "Searching Again for the Sacred," *Time*, April 9, 1973, pp. 90-93.

7. Jay W. Forrester, "Churches at the Transition between Growth and World Equilibrium," *Zygon* 7 (1972): 145-67, makes this point clear on p. 159.

8. Anthony F. C. Wallace, "Rituals: Sacred and Profane," *Zygon* 1 (1966): 60-81.

9. Ralph Wendell Burhoe, "Five Steps in the Evolution of Man's Knowledge of Good and Evil," *Zygon* 2 (1967): 77-96; also chap. 3 herein.

10. Walter B. Cannon, *The Wisdom of the Body* (New York: W. W. Norton & Co., 1932).

11. Donald T. Campbell, in an unpublished manuscript distributed to a graduate course at Northwestern University, winter 1970, quoted in Ralph Wendell Burhoe, "The Phenomenon of Religion Seen Scientifically," in *Changing Perspectives in the Scientific Study of Religion*, ed. Allan Eister (New York: Wiley Interscience, 1974), chap. 1; and in Ralph Wendell Burhoe, ed., *Science and Human Values in the 21st Century* (Philadelphia: Westminster Press, 1971), p. 144.

12. *Science and Human Values in the 21st Century* contains a brief account of the inscription of information about human purposes in man's brain from his genotype (pp. 27-31) and from the religious elements of his culture (pp. 141-52); Cf also chap. 6 of this book, section, *The Brain as the Yoke*. . . . The technical meaning of "ecological niche" which I am using here has been defined in my "The Control of Behavior: Human and Environmental," *Journal of Environmental Health* 35 (1972): 249. It should be noted that my definition of human purpose given here is very close to that given by Hefner at the end of his paper in *Zygon* 8 (1973): 395-411.

13. Van A. Harvey, *A Handbook of Theological Terms* (New York: Macmillian Co., 1964), p. 106.

14. Ibid., p. 181.

15. Isaiah 55:8-9.

16. Ralph Wendell Burhoe, "Natural Selection and God," *Zygon* 7 (1972): 30-63; also reprinted here as chap. 4.

17. For recent views concerning evolution as random variations finding ever-new levels of complex organization, see J. Bronowski, "New Concepts in the Evolution of Complexity: Stratified Stability and Unbounded Plans," *Zygon* 5 (1970): 18-35.

18. Thomas Kuhn, *The Structure of Scientific Revolutions* (Chicago: University of Chicago Press, 1962).

19. Erwin Schrödinger, *What is Life?* (Cambridge: Cambridge University Press, 1944; New York: Doubleday & Co., 1956); Norbert Weiner, *Human Use of Human Beings: Cybernetics and Society* (Boston: Houghton Mifflin Co., 1950).

20. Bronowski (n. 17 above), p. 33.

21. Herbert A. Simon, *The Sciences of the Artificial* (Cambridge, Mass.: M.I.T. Press, 1969); W. Ross Ashby, *A Design for a Brain: The Origin of Adaptive Behavior* (New York: John Wiley & Sons, 1960).

22. See, for instance, Tillich's assertions about man's incapacities to probe the nature of *god* without running into an infinite regress of further corrections of his statements. Cf., e.g., *Systematic Theology*, 3 vols. (Chicago: University of Chicago Press, 1951-63), 1:81.

23. Theodosius Dobzhansky, "An Essay on Religion, Death, and Evolutionary Adaptation," *Zygon* 1 (1966): 317-31.

24. Burhoe (n. 9 above).

25. Donald T. Campbell, "Variations and Selective Retention in Socio-Cultural Evolution," in H. R. Barringer, G. I. Blanksten, and R. W. Mack eds., *Social Change in Developing Areas: A Reinterpretation of Evolutionary Theory* (Cambridge, Mass.: Schenkman Publishing Co., 1965), reprinted in *General Systems* 14 (1969): 69-85. The pool of culturetypes would be analogous to the pool of genotypes for *Homo sapiens*. The pool of culturetypes is close to the Popper concept of World 3 reported by J. C. Eccles in *Zygon* 8 (1973): 282-293.

26. Alfred E. Emerson, "Dynamic Homeostasis: A Unifying Principle in Organic, Social, and Ethical Evolution," *Zygon* 3 (1968): 129-68.

27. Burhoe (n. 9 above); Donald T. Campbell, "On the Genetics of Altruism and the Counter-hedonic Components in Human Nature," *Journal*

of Social Issues 28, no. 3 (1972): 21-37; and n. 26 above. See also Dob-zhansky, *Zygon* 8 (1973): 269.

28. See Burhoe, "Control of Behavior" (n. 12 above), esp. p. 249, for a brief summary of the view of life (including human life) as open systems of flow patterns shaped by boundary conditions. A key paper in an expanding new literature on this new view of life is found in Aharon Katchalsky's "Thermodynamics of Flow and Biological Organization," *Zygon* 6 (1971): 99-125.

29. See n. 7 above.

30. Campbell (n. 27 above) gives a recent and important analysis of this as a problem in human genetics, and Emerson (n. 26 above) gives an excellent general picture for evolution and social behavior.

6

*The Source of Civilization in the Natural Selection of Coadapted Information in Genes and Culture**

In concluding this issue of *Zygon: Journal of Religion and Science,* featuring Donald T. Campbell's presidential address to the American Psychological Association, "On the Conflicts between Biological and Social Evolution and between Psychology and Moral Tradition," I, as editor as well as author, have been tempted to defend his primary theses by correcting the multitudinous errors that I see in the negative responses published in the May 1976 issue of the *American Psychologist* and elsewhere. To me, most of the negative responses evidence a failure to read Campbell with sufficient care or with sufficient background in recent interdisciplinary developments of evolutionary theory to be able to understand fully or correctly what he is saying. But republication of his address in *Zygon* demands a more positive response, for Campbell's paper conforms with and amplifies our basic hypotheses that have been reiterated in editorials and papers for more than ten years.

Also, Campbell's presidential address may mark a new age in the history of psychology and of psychotherapy. Speaking "from a scientific, physicalistic (materialistic) world view," he has pointed to how a most plausible and hardheaded science of human behavior can embrace in a coherent and empirically validated conceptual system a spectrum of data that ranges

*This paper was written as a conclusion for the *Zygon* issue on *Religion's Role in the Context of Genetic and Cultural Evolution,* 11(3): 263-303, September 1976, which republished Donald T. Campbell's presidential address to the American Psychological Association in 1975 together with a number of not previously published responses thereto.

from the DNA substrate of organism at one extreme to religious myth and theology at the other. He has pioneered in the seemingly impossible synthesis of this broad range of intellectual perspectives upon human behavior. To some it is frighteningly incredible or incomprehensible. At one extreme, his use of the genetic mechanics prohibiting altruism may symbolize the lowest level of reductionism, beyond the pale of psychology, even for most of those in the biobehavioral wing. The opposite extreme, pointing to scientific grounds for the essential validity of what currently appear to many as "insubstantial" religious myths, is likewise beyond the pale, even for most in the humanistic and social wing of psychology.

I believe there is a high probability that further studies will justify the hypothesis of the connectibility of these extremes under a putatively common selective system. Such a selective system has been postulated by a number of scientists as the intrinsically steady states of natural systems as they evolve hierarchically.[1] These naturally stable states of subatomic particles constitute atoms, of atoms constitute molecules, of molecules constitute complex molecules, of complex molecules constitute living cells, of living cells constitute organisms, of organisms constitute species, of species constitute ecosystems. J. Bronowski has suggested intriguingly that random variations of elements at previously attained levels of this hierarchy of structures are exactly what force the emergence or development of the next level of stability or "being."[2] B. F. Skinner has noted that this kind of selection operates not only in the phylogeny of the evolution of species but equally in the ontogeny of human behavior.[3]

While a scientific understanding of the integration of the levels of cybernetic mechanisms of complex systems is not yet too far along, there would seem to be sufficient promise to justify Campbell's suggestion that our understanding of human behavior thus may be extended in a scientific system, map, or model that actually embraces the wide range from genes to religious culture.

For psychology, the development of a comprehensive and coherent theoretical model could mean the beginning of the end of the different "cultures" that segregate psychology into different university departments and buildings as well as into discrete societies and journals that have little in common intellectual structure beyond their claim to be describing some aspects of human experience/behavior. Much more than that, it could mean the beginning of psychology as *a science* in the usual science of a discipline possessed of an empirically validated theoretical structure which can indeed explain or account for and not simply describe, categorize, and correlate patterns of human experience/behavior.

For the general culture, the development suggested by Campbell could mean a more effective science for application to psychotherapy or the "cure of souls," since it would encompass a wider range of the actual individual and social requirements for viability or well-being.

At present, psychology might be said to be a bird with two wings—one biological and the other sociocultural—but the bird cannot coordinate the two wings sufficiently to fly much above the empirical ground level of some interesting categories of often not too high correlations between inputs and outputs of some obviously not homogeneous black boxes. I think Campbell shows realistically how psychology might become the integrating link between man's biological and social natures.

My strong espousal of Campbell's address is because of his largely sound and interdisciplinary scientific extension of the analysis of human behavior from a central position in psychology to integrate with the analyses provided in terms as basic as genetics on the one side and as high as religion on the other. I am not saying that each one of his many suggested conceptual details is a final picture. His own cautious statements in his address and his tentativeness in personal discussion make it clear to me that he is more skeptical about some of them than I am. While I would challenge a number of points, including a small misinterpretation of something he attributes to me, all these would be picayune relative to the major sweep of what his address accomplishes, and I will not discuss them here.

But, since his address covers an area in which I also have been working for some decades, I should like to provide some additional support for his general position, as some of the other authors in this issue have done. I shall seek to extend Campbell's schema further in each of the directions in which he has pushed from the psychosocial center.

Since my primary concern is one of constructive understandings of religion and advancement of its salvatory functions in the light of the sciences, I shall seek to extend and go beyond his interpretation of the function of religion to provide a socially cooperative behavior that genes alone cannot accomplish. I shall propose a mechanism to explain how religion's function to catalyze cooperative social behavior in fact can be selected in a "culturetype" (the human societal organism's analogue of a genotype), when such behavior cannot be selected in a genotype (the genetic recipe for an organism). I shall go further to show that, as in biology there have been selected mechanisms to give pleasure as well as pain, so there has been selected in the sociocultural evolution of religion a pleasant, hopeful, promissory aspect as well as a fearful and inhibitory aspect and that the former aspect is even more effective to generate cooperation. Also, I shall suggest an explanation of why we may say that even the "intelligent" variations—the varied, conscious decisions of men, which Campbell says (but many of his critics failed to note) are a part of the diversity upon which the natural-selection analogues of sociocultural evolution operate[4]—are themselves tantamount to "blind variations" among which in the end a more-than-human *nature* selects, no matter how conscious, rational, or even scientific the humans may be in their choice making.

In the other direction I shall seek also to extend the integration of Campbell's model even beyond the information encoded in the DNA of the genes to the prebiological cosmos, that is, into physics. By this extension I shall go further than Campbell does. Not only shall I assert the functional utility of religion for social cooperation, I shall move toward demonstrating that the conceptual schemes or myths of religion—about superhuman gods who punish the doers of certain evils and reward the good—that have been selected in cultural evolution are perhaps truer, not only more necessary for societal functioning but also more valid as "ontological" hypotheses, than most modern intellectuals have supposed. This will bring my extension of the conceptual scheme full circle around the world of man's conceptual thought to the antipodes from where Campbell writes of the psychosocial sciences to where theology and physics are found merged in a *pacific* ocean. I seek to present a world map where all realms of man's "vocabularies" are represented on the surface of a coherent globe of man's cognitive experience, through and around which there are multitudinous potential lines of logical connection.

I shall go as far as to suggest that not only was it necessary and valid for the selection processes in sociocultural evolution to produce the religions it did in order to generate cooperative behavior functional for human society, since genes alone are incapable of generating it, but that it was necessary for the selection processes of sociocultural evolution to develop those religions in the ways and in the times they did—prior to the flowering of the brain and culture to produce conscious, rational, and scientific thought—in order to make possible the flowering of recent high civilization.

At the same time I shall point out that the rapidly declining power of religion in the world today to provide the necessary understandings of the self in the scheme of things, in order to generate sound psyches and motivate adequate morals for a civilized society, stems from religion's lack of a theology or system of understanding and interpretation that is coadapted with contemporary scientific information. I shall seek also to show that the secular and political philosophies are relatively impotent to do this because they are not, as religions have been, coadapted with the information in the human gene pool through ancient ritual ties to the lower, more specifically genetically programmed levels of the brain.

I believe this picture will show that our twentieth-century crisis in human evolution is either a stress that will *select against* most contemporary sociocultural systems and possibly bring on a much more catastrophic Dark Ages than those after the fall of Rome or, if our readiness to adapt can become consciously motivated in time, a stress to move us to avoid the slower and more painful processes of prior levels of sociocultural evolution and enter more immediately into a new level of sociocultural evolution guided by a *coadapted science and religion*. The latter is something which Greco-Roman civilization almost, but not quite, succeeded in accomplishing in time to avoid its fall. In either case, I believe there will emerge a new coadaptation of science with religion, analogous to the synthesis of neo-

Platonism and Aristotelianism with a Jewish religious cult, which, I have suggested, made Western theology the ground for Western civilization and science.[5] Our similar problem now is how to provide morals for society and meaning for psyche by a proper coadaptation of science and religion today before the collapse of Western and a dawning World civilization.

Zygon for more than ten years has been affirming that the time has come when the sciences can provide new light on religious questions and human salvation, that there is at hand a new "revelation" for religious truth. This means that effective theologians, like effective psychologists and psychotherapists, need to become aware of new knowledge from whatever scientific disciplines that may illuminate our understanding of human nature and its place in the scheme of things. This may require some technical information of new kinds to be integrated within the corpus of both psychology and theology.

A Note on the Nature and Use of Scientific Knowledge

In his introduction Campbell pointed to a limitation on the experimental method in the arena of psychology and psychiatry that prevents them, relative to some other sciences, from advancing more rapidly to truly assured doctrine. He has suggested that, if traditional religious recipes for living have undergone a long period of winnowing by nature's selective processes of what really works, as has genetic wisdom, perhaps we have at hand a truth and wisdom about and for human behavior that is more adequate than some of the speculations of the psychosocial sciences in the past century.

Here we may say he was implying that when scientific theory cannot be checked or validated for soundness by experiment it may be validated by observation. In astronomy some of our most valid science arose without man's being able experimentally to manipulate the variables involved in the motions of the planets. In evolutionary theory about the origins and development of the earth, chemicals, and species we have built up a very significant body of assured doctrine about events in a time prior even to our capacity to observe what was going on, to say nothing about our experimentally manipulating any of the variables. While suitable experimental manipulation and/or wisely selected observations of certain of the variables under suitable conditions have provided confirmations of our scientific theories (conceptual structures or symbolic models) of the real world, it is not always necessary to be able to experiment or even to observe an action or entity to have relatively sound knowledge about it and its history. If from other sources we already have a well-validated model, we can, by operating the proper logical (mathematical) formulas in a brain or a computer, derive from limited observable elements certain conclusions about a more complex system that are as sound and true as our model is valid, as the Greek geometers long ago discovered. Central to scientific as well as to genetic information is a tried and tested model of the real world.

What I am seeking to suggest to theologians is that the wide-ranging, partially integrated models of the contemporary sciences have built an understanding of the nature of cosmic and human history that far exceeds the scope of any previous revelations. Furthermore, I am suggesting that proper attention to the wider ranges of scientific knowledge as they disclose man's nature and place in the scheme of things may provide theologians with a new hermeneutic, allowing them to correlate scientific understanding more effectively with the cumulation of earlier religious revelations of the sacred. From my first editorial in *Zygon* I have claimed that the new hierophanies potentially provided by the light of the sciences will not so much destroy the traditional ones as enhance them. This has been a traditional claim of many reformers and advancers both of religion and science. It is to such a humility and genuine respect in the presence of the long-evolved and well-winnowed wisdom of previous doctrines of man and his salvation that Campbell calls his colleagues in the name of a more scientific stance.

The Brain as The Yoke that Binds Genes and Cultures

To understand the conversion of a genetically selfish animal into a cooperator in the world's first widely extended cooperative societies (some of them nearly species-wide, so far as their sampling of the range of human gene pool is concerned), an understanding of the brain is central. R. W. Sperry has reminded us that the central agency in human behavior, feeling, and thinking of all kinds is the brain.[6] E. O. Wilson at the end of his monumental *Sociobiology* has suggested that a coalition of biogenetics and neurophysiology probably will be necessary for a science of society.[7] For decades Hudson Hoagland has been telling theologians and philosophers that religion is an almost inevitable result of the way the brain has evolved to provide viable organic responses to internal and external conditions. The brain is an organ of survival established by biological evolution. Its main function has been to enable the organism to integrate both external and internal sensory information into configurations that will enable the organism to adapt and remain viable: "The ability to form meaningful configurations that encompass large segments of the environment [what Wilson calls 'tracking the environment'] is a property of the more highly developed brains, and a good case can be made for the view that man's concerns with science, philosophy, political ideologies and theologies are a reflection of a basic property of his nervous system to integrate extensive configurations relating himself to his environment."[8]

The brain's activities are structured in two ways. First, the brain is structured from the inside out by the genetic code inside each of its ten billion cells. This code contains a memory of successful ways to live, culled or selected from a long history of life in past environments. The memory units have been integrated or coadapted with one another and relative to a wide range of internal and environing circumstances.

Second, the brain's activities are structured from the outside in by all the messages received from its environment, beginning during its development in embryo and continuing until death. In the human brain there is a special genetic adaptation thus to receive a large block of information from a specially structured, living record of cultural information, environmentally stored in the "social organism" and its artifacts, a new "supraorganism" with which each human has become symbiotic and on which he is dependent for his life. This cultural input is the socially transmitted patterning of the mores or traditions of a society which takes place in accord with special sequences of enculturation. Both prelinguistic and linguistic information are transmitted this way. Recent ethology and psychology have shown how these inputs must be in phase with a hierarchy of levels of development or maturation of the brain, beginning with early "imprinting," through social conditioning or reinforcement, to later reasoning. George Edgin Pugh has given a well worked-out picture of the human brain as the central agent in our "value-driven decision system" and has called the genetically determined values our "primary values" and the values shaped by the input to the brain from the outside our "secondary values."[9]

Paul D. MacLean has shown that our brains are structured in three layers which originated in three different periods of our evolution.[10] The first and lowest level he calls our reptilian brain because it originated when our ancestors were reptile-like creatures. From the brains of contemporary reptiles and other evidence we know that this level of the brain contains the basic mechanisms which produce automatic or instinctive behavior to keep the animal (including the human animal) alive and in good condition. It seems to be *basic* for most of our higher responses, or our motivations in response, to messages from our inner states as well as from our environment. Its nearly automatic response patterns to certain kinds of messages from the environment provide the basis for ritual (behavioral or prelinguistic) communication. Genetic selection has insured that our reptilian brain automatically produces behavior that statistically is geared to enhance life. We do not become conscious of much of this behavior, in ourselves even, until we begin to study scientifically the various mechanisms involved.

The second major level of the human brain's structure and behavior MacLean has called our paleomammalian or old mammalian brain because it originated in and still resembles the brain structures and functions that began to cover the reptilian neural structures as the mammals emerged in evolutionary development. This mammalian brain provides a more generalized picture of the self in relation to the environment together with suitable emotions or feelings that provide a more generalized guide for directing behavior than the more tightly prescribed, automatic responses provided by our reptilian brain. It provides the mechanisms that produce our feelings of fear and love toward prospective conditions, on the basis of which we can choose alternative courses. This old mammalian brain level in man appears to integrate information from the inside of the organism (including its various needs) with information from the outside world (with its various opportunities for satisfying needs) and to be "essential for a feeling of individuality and personal identity."[11] These feelings are basic to our religious and moral responses toward right and wrong.

The third level of the human brain is the neocortex, which has developed phenomenally in *Homo* during the last million years and made it possible for man to be different from all other creatures. The development of the neocortex is *genetically* so structured that the *genotype* provides a still more loosely coupled and more generalized control of behavior than the mammalian brain in response to information from the sense organs of the world within and outside the body. There seems to be good evidence that this outer cortex or "bark" of the brain provides for the ready reception with significant meaning of more complex prelinguistic and linguistic symbols from the environing culture. It provides for the association of these symbols with the underlying organic or ritual meanings aroused in response to patterns of our outside and inside worlds received from our various senses and given varied affective tone through connections in the mammalian and reptilian levels of our brain. The neocortex also provides us with a neurological mechanism for complex elaboration and logical manipulation of symbolic structures which we call ideas. The mechanism for manipulating ideas or symbols includes ways of projecting them against the patterns of remembered ideas from earlier experiences as well as against the genetically and culturally prescribed norms that have been inscribed previously in the central nervous system. On the basis of a genetically and culturally inscribed program for computing consequences (akin to the consequences of moves on a chessboard), the symbols can be manipulated to relate a current sequence to a potential future sequence, and, insofar as the models in the brain conform to the real world, we can bring possible future states into our present decisions—a matter of great importance to religion. These mechanisms embrace our emotionally conditioned and genetically programmed instinctive needs that motivate our choices. By making possible linguistic communication, the neocortex provides a new level of social transmission of culturally evolved and inherited information that has greatly enriched our genetic heritage.

These three levels of brain under proper enculturation of the neocortex are coordinated and produce harmonious hierarchical operations of behaviors, feelings, and capacities for rational thought that allow our living to be directed simultaneously by genes, the world, and society. But it is also important to note that they are all heavily interconnected and work together in what might be called a coadapted, interdependent fashion. It is such a relationship that provides an explanation of the psychosomatic relationship between physiological behavior and states of mind. The recent addition of the new cortex in man also permits an explanation of how man can be programmed simultaneously by his own basic and bodily needs as registered in his genes and his reptilian brain and yet also by the highly complex patterns of social cooperation that can be enculturated through the outer cortex into almost "instinctive" self-giving to the sociocultural system. It is this evolution of the outer cortex of the human brain that is necessary to explain how human evolution emerged to a new level of life above that of all other creatures on earth and why man is the first to be able to motivate social cooperation with non-kin segments of the same species.

The Genetic Problem

But how could the genes structuring the brain evolve this way if it is true that the natural selection of alternative alleles cannot favor a competing genetic heritage? I have long shared the understanding presented so dramatically in Campbell's paper that biogenetic evolution by itself cannot produce self-giving behavior that benefits other individuals who are in genetic competition. I shall make it clear at the outset that for my doctrine of man for a scientifically credible theology I find it even more important to accept the stark genetic model presented by George C. Williams than does perhaps Wilson for his sociobiology or Campbell for his biosocial psychology.[12] My grounds for this derive in part from the new information on the brain as well as from reflection on the problems of historical theology and the evolution of religion. I shall develop my reasons for understanding the evolution of religion, more or less as sketched by Campbell, as the "missing link" for understanding how apemen became human. This in turn leads me to an understanding of why men must continue to cultivate a higher level of religion with a credible theology if they are to remain human in a sociocultural system informed by science and scientific technology.

The seemingly devastating evidence against altruism pictured in Campbell's quotation from the zoologist Michael Ghiselin is, in my view, valid information which cannot be avoided except by those whose understanding is limited or confused.[13] Since religious belief is motivational for personal and social salvation only when it is believed to be true and carried out in deed, a confused and incredible understanding could not generate adequately strong religious convictions in a population that was persuaded of the validity of any seemingly controverting scientific pictures. Like Campbell, I do not fear the "hard" truth that has scientific validation, and I make more sense of the traditional religious wisdom in this light than in the sentimental, anthropocentric, subjective, wish-fulfilling dogma of some recent liberal humanism and social theory. Therefore, I count it as gain rather than loss to concur largely with Williams's picture of the hard genetic rule that the natural selection of competing alleles cannot produce within a species social altruism that extends significantly beyond close relatives.

Actually, my solution to the perplexing puzzle of how to explain human sociality within established scientific concepts takes its cue from Williams. His *Adaptation and Natural Selection* already pointed out that the genetically evolved brain is a necessary part of the explanation.[14] He also pointed out that the general solution is akin to that of the adaptation of any species to an environment, that is, to an ecosystem which includes other species that may offer support as well as competition. In fact, it is to account for such adaptations to an environment that genetic and evolutionary theory has developed.

While Williams, on genetic grounds, asserted "that group-related adaptations do not, in fact, exist," he did not overlook the fact that there are complex human societies, and he specifically pointed out that man was an "apparent exception to the rule that the natural selection of individuals cannot produce group-related adaptations. This exception may be found in animals that live in stable social groups and have the intelligence and other mental qualities necessary to form a system of personal friendships and animosities that transcend the limits of family relationship. . . . Primitive man lived in a world in which stable interactions of personalities were very much a part of his ecological environment. He had to adjust to this set of ecological factors as well as to any other."[15]

While Williams gives a few suggestions on how a human brain could recognize friends and the possibility of reciprocal benefits whereby one distant cousin might be induced to repay help received from another in time of trouble, his *Adaptation and Natural Selection* hardly mentions how in a population of brains the information about and motivation for these mutually beneficial behaviors are selected and transmitted in human social evolution, except in a brief passage saying "this one ape . . . was transferred by evolution [of his enlarged brain, manual dexterity, etc.] from an ordinary animal, with an ordinary existence, to a cultural chain reaction."[16] The cultural chain reaction is now what we need to explain in more detail. But we must explain it always in the context of a population of individual animals whose basic values or norms for behaving are encoded in their genes and whose social values—no matter how highly civilized—statistically can never be programmed against what their genetic heritage requires, namely, survival of the genetic line. For, without a gene pool that can develop a phenotype with human capacities, there would be no human culture whatever.

Wilson's *Sociobiology* gives a wealth of detail on the evolution of sociality that is not given by Williams, and *Sociobiology* is a "must" reference for all who would work on social behavior, including morals and religion. But the basic theoretical problem that runs through Wilson's work is the problem which Campbell faced in his paper and which was so cogently expressed by Williams: How could genetic competition ever result in cooperation? *Sociobiology* provides a highly informed development of some of the basic elements and possible solutions to this problem, such as those suggested by Williams above and some of those that have been developed in this and other issues of *Zygon* and other places. Probably nowhere has there been such a concentrated and comprehensive treatment especially of the biological factors as in *Sociobiology,* a primer for a burgeoning, new field.

A process to explain aspects of human sociocultural evolution in the context of the established genetic factors has been roughly outlined from varied perspectives by Campbell, F. T. Cloak, Edward C. Uliassi, and Robert Boyd and Peter J. Richerson in this issue of *Zygon*. But the addition of information on the evolution of the brain and its operation as simultaneously the seat of the genetically and socioculturally transmitted values, I believe, will extend the explanation of how it is that civilized man could evolve under natural selection and why it is that natural selection is, as I previously have suggested, an excellent, modern symbol for man's creator and judge at all levels of his existence in which his animal nature is united with his higher nature.[17]

If we agree that genetics alone cannot produce large urban societies within a species except among individuals with identical genotypes as in the colonial coelenterata or individuals of very close kin (or otherwise on the basis of genetically noncompeting sterile castes within a close-kin population) as in the social insects, how is it that *Homo sapiens* did succeed in developing societies that spread far beyond the primitive, close-kin tribal societies of our ancestors? How does it happen that empirically we find socially cooperative and self-denying behavior, sometimes even the voluntary self-sacrifice on the part of many of the finest specimens for the sake of a complex group of many thousands or even millions of other individuals most of whom are not as closely related as tenth cousins, to say nothing of being as close as brothers?

Two factors have to be involved. First is insurance that the genetic line that produces such behavior is not eliminated in competition. This is tantamount to agreeing with Ghiselin and Williams that there cannot be any altruism or self-sacrifice of the real core or seed that transmits our nature from one generation to another, and I do this gladly since it fits some facts of evolved religion which I shall mention later. Mean-

while, as Campbell and others have noted above, the possibility
for cooperating and yet benefiting one's genetic line is provided in what is called reciprocal altruism, a notion that has
been developed by Robert L. Trivers but to which Williams
already pointed in 1966: Since, with his brain's elaborated
capacities, man "recognizes his benefactor and remembers the
help provided, [he] will probably reciprocate some day. A
number of people, including Darwin, have recognized the
importance of this factor in human evolution. Darwin speaks of
it as the 'lowly motive' of helping others in the hope of future
repayment. I see no reason why a conscious motive need be
involved. It is necessary that help provided to others be occa-
sionally reciprocated if it is to be favored by natural selection.
It is not necessary that either the giver or the receiver be aware
of this."[18]

Williams seems a bit ambiguous here as to whether he is
talking of natural selection of genes or of cultural patterns.
Campbell, Wilson, and others clearly have posited the natural
selection of a cultural pattern that is independent of or at least
not specified by the gene pool. Certainly, the specificities of
different human languages, technologies, and religions are not
structured by genes. Certainly, these cultural patterns evolve
and seem to be selected at the unconscious levels posited by
both Williams and authors in this issue of *Zygon*. But Williams
does not specify mechanisms for the selection of sociocultural
patterns independently of the genetic patterns.

This mechanism for sociocultural inheritance is the second
factor that I suggest must be involved to account for the
evolution of man's patterns of social cooperation in specialized
roles with conspecifics with whom he is not closely genetically
related. It is at this point that the writers in this issue of *Zygon*
are going beyond Williams and the "central dogma" of the new
DNA genetics, even though basically agreeing with them concerning the underlying mechanisms. Only in recent millennia
have human sociocultural systems expanded appreciably
beyond kinfolk tribes to draw together in cities the populations
of reciprocally cooperating individuals ranging from thousands
to now millions, representing generous samples of species-wide
distributions of genetic types. Because an essentially complete
sociocultural transformation can take place within a genera-

tion, it cannot, simply because the change is so rapid, be explained on the basis of genetic information. But the important problem is that it cannot be explained genetically in principle and requires something of a "miracle" to show how the gene-selecting mechanisms that prohibit enhancing a competing genetic line have seemed to be overcome.

Genetic Selection Can Favor Interspecific Cooperation in Ecological Communities

My contribution to explaining this starts with the acceptance of the orthodox pictures of neo-Darwinian and biochemical evolution but adds a hypothesis that has been stimulated by some other hard biological facts that have been provided in my discussions of these problems with Alfred E. Emerson over the past twenty-five years.[19] The model for my hypothesis for the mechanism for sociocultural evolution as an independent system of memory (inheritance), of variation (both blind [unconscious] and perceived [consciously planned]), and of selection (whether blind or consciously planned) comes from the model of *symbiosis,* the mutual adaptation of different kinds (species) of creatures to provide by their mutual contributions a resulting ecosystem giving more viability to each of the component species than would be possessed by any one of them alone.

In this kind of evolutionary change the prohibition posed by gene competition against selection for social cooperation is bypassed as clearly as it is in the case of the social insects or family cooperation, but by very different mechanisms. In the social insects and close-kin selection there is a clear genetic gain rather than a competition when genes operate to program phenotypes that cooperate to extend a common genetic line. In some cases, bodily self-sacrifice for siblings may and does enhance that line. In symbiosis, however, two different species are involved. Their community of cooperative behavior does not arise directly from competition among the genes within any one of the species. Instead, each species is separated from allelic competition by the fact of being genetically isolated from the other species. It also is isolated from interspecific competition by being in a different ecological niche. This opens up the potential for the genes within each of the separate species to compete exactly toward an improved interspecific adaptation as a more effective cooperating agent in an interspecific ecosystem. Here the cooperative, specialized roles of each species may produce an ecosystem that is more efficient or adaptive for each of the several species involved than would be the case of any single species seeking to perform all the functions necessary for life in the physical habitat.

The case on which Emerson has provided great illumination is that of the mutual cooperation of species in an ecological community. While he has written much on this since, I quote a nice statement of the situation from his presidential address to the Ecological Society of America in 1941:

. . . the social insect colony is an interspecific ecological community consisting of numerous species of plants and animals adjusted both parasitically and symbiotically to the internal environment of the supraorganism. [L. R.] Cleveland has shown that the wood-eating roach and termite communities were fundamentally functional adjustments promoting an efficient cooperation between the wood-eating insects and their symbiotic cellulose-digesting intestinal protozoa. In order that the molted individual could become reinfected with [the interdependent] protozoa, it was necessary for such an individual to live in a family or social community. Thus evolution has resulted in an integrated, balanced, biological system incorporating organisms of various species and various organismic levels, in its entirety exhibiting dynamic equilibrium between its parts and with its external environment.[20]

Instructive for understanding interspecific cooperation approaching complete interdependence and cooperation is the case of the social termites, which emerged from family systems of primitive roaches to find a more viable ecological niche in symbiosis with species of flagellate protozoa. The flagellates flourished better in the more protected environment, and an effective supply of their food was found by inhabiting the digestive tract of the wood-eating termite. The protozoa could metabolize wood cellulose to provide more than enough food for themselves. The surplus product enabled their termite host to be nourished by the wood—thus a plenteous source of food. The symbiosis of these two very different species is an adaptation, accomplished by the gene pool of each species separately, but in relation to a common external environment, an adaptation to an ecosystem in which mutually beneficial functions with other species are not only possible but common.

This adaptation of two independent species into a common system that embraces both of them (and also other species), a system that may make each species completely dependent upon and "devoted to" the needs of the other, as in the case of termites and their flagellates, is a symbiotic reciprocal cooperation. The mutuality of advantages for the respective species—given by the new ecological niches into which their symbiosis allows them to move—has been selected and recorded in DNA codons by the same system of natural selection of genes that selects all living systems. Williams calls such symbiotic evolution within an ecosystem a "biotic *evolution*," as distinguished from "organic evolution." Since the information that structures or provides the patterns of such mutually beneficial relations among the various biological species living within the physical environment of a habitat seems to be found only within the gene pools of the several adapted species, Williams does not want to call this "biotic *adaptation*."[21]

However, this refusal to call a viable ecosystem "adaptive" seems to be a misleading restriction on the term "adaptation" that arbitrarily cuts off from genetic theory the operation of interspecific coadaptation which one would suppose geneticists would be as proud to proclaim as they are the very effective explanatory model of intraspecific or intragenotypic *coadaptation*.

The indirect (secondary) epistatic effects of multiple interacting forces in a genotype generate outcomes that are different from the mere sum of the direct effects of each of the individual forces. Since selection operates on the total system of forces interacting, the result tends to be the selection of the coadaptedness of the multiple genic sources whose interaction generates living systems. Emergent adaptive traits of whole systems, whether intraspecific or interspecific, occur. This requires that one read the presence of the several gene pools of the several interacting species in a common habitat as a system of coadapted information units that collectively operate as the integrated unit that, in fact, does structure the ecosystem and its adaptation. To be sure, the integrated information generating the symbiotic group is selected by, and only by, the survival of the particular genes that remain in the competition carried on within some particular species, as Williams insists it must be. There is no conflict here.

But, if we take into account the fact that a particular species functionally is coadapted with other species in a symbiotic community of an ecosystem, then that information which instructs the biota is also selected and stored in the collectivity of the gene pools of the several interdependent species. The coadapted selection of these several information banks is a program that promotes the success of the biota as well as that of the organisms of the different species that constitute it, insofar as the organisms of the different species, in fact, do constitute a reciprocally functioning or interdependent net in an ecosystem.

The selection of a biota is not "group selection" within a species from competing genes. I am perhaps more convinced than Williams that it is "tautologically" as well as factually impossible for genes to be selected that confer an advantage on their competitors. But Williams points to the fact that it is quite clear that competition among alleles (different forms of the same gene) in a population is exactly what produces that population's adaptation to its environment, to an optimal role in an ecosystem consisting of other functioning species as well as of certain physical characteristics. In those cases where mutual adaptations of a *group* of species that cooperate to constitute an ecosystem do provide greater viability for the several species than is otherwise possible, the interspecific collectivity of coadapted genes is a *biotic adaptation* just as clearly as the intragenotypic collectivity of coadapted genes of any particular organism is an *organic adaptation,* even though the former could not occur apart from the latter.

Nongenetic Information in Evolution

Because the informing mechanisms or boundary conditions that shape the flow patterns of energy and materials that we know as life are in the last analysis more than those contained in the genes, and since a larger picture helps us to understand our place in the scheme of things, I wish at this juncture to point out some of the new perspective on evolution that goes beyond that of many of the neo-Darwinians. A number of scientists have approached the problem of life systems with a more physicalistic and information-science view, within which genetic fitness naturally falls as a subclass. The larger picture presents living systems in terms of the physics of metastable patterns in thermodynamic flows. The cybernetic guidance provided by the genetic code over the behavior of other molecules in a cell *is only one of many mechanisms* that exist in nature to provide metastable states far from thermodynamic equilibrium, although it is clearly a primary kind of document for life on earth.[22]

Among nonliving cybernetic mechanisms, for instance, is the water cycle of the earth, which returns ocean water as rain to the highlands and keeps our rivers flowing and fills our lakes. Such general, steady-state-maintaining mechanisms, which natural forces determine or select, existed long before they evolved to such higher levels as the DNA controls for the dynamic flows of matter energy in organisms. The norms, boundary conditions, or controls of the stable patterns of preliving flows, such as rivers and lakes, not only are selected but evolve with changing environmental conditions, as when mountains are lifted and valleys deepen. Much evidence has been accumulated to show how energy flow patterns character-ize all dynamic systems from prebiological to the most refined operations of the human mind and sociocultural system. An interesting and graphic view of some common principles of energy-matter flow in the broad range from solar energy to complex human societies, including religions, has been pre-sented by Howard T. Odum in his *Environment, Power, and Society*.[23]

The same general system of physical nature is involved in the accounts by the molecular biologists of the various interactions of DNA and its environment to produce the characteristic activities of the living cell. And as Bronowski puts it: "There are evolutionary processes in nature which do not demand the intervention of selective forces [in the limited or neo-Darwinian sense]. Characteristic is the evolution of the chemi-cal elements. . . . Here then is a physical model which shows how simple units come together to make more complex config-urations; how these configurations, if they are stable, serve as units to make higher configurations. . . . The sequence of building up stratified stability is also clear in living forms. Atoms build the four base molecules [that] are built into the nucleic acids, which are remarkably stable in their turn. And the genes are stable structures formed from the nucleic acids, and so on . . . to the complete cell."[24]

For a larger picture of the truth about human life, not only do we need to go to the *pre*biological, underlying physical circumstances and laws which have created the stable dynamic systems found there—such as the lakes for habitats or the stereochemical structures for genotypes and phenotypes—but also we must look into the operations that are going on at levels that more recently have emerged than the DNA codes to structure our behavior.

Living organisms are, much more than we have previously acknowledged, dependent for life-sustaining behavior upon information that is not in the chromosomes. Of course, there have long been a number of biologists who have kept to the fore the importance of cytoplasmic agencies of inheritance. There have been interesting hypotheses with supporting evidence for understanding the eucaryotic cell as a symbiosis of formerly independent and separate lines of evolving systems, some of them carrying nucleic acid information independent of the chromosomes. Also, one does not know how much non-nucleic-acid information there may be within a cell, including the genetic repressors and metabolic controls constructed of amino acids. Many have questioned the possibility that even the tremendous amount of information carried in the genes could be capable of specifying the stupendous amount of information that cells and organisms obviously possess. The epigenetic differentiation of the special cell types in multicellular organisms certainly requires information not found in the genotype. Howard H. Pattee and associates in *Hierarchy Theory* have presented a promising analysis of how to understand the problem of the organized complexity of living systems. Their view suggests that the maintenance and development of the organized complexity of living systems do not lie in any one level, such as the genotypic description, but come from an interacting hierarchy of levels of structural and descriptive systems. One of the associates, Herbert A. Simon, had earlier written that an organism, even a man, "as a behaving system is quite simple. The apparent complexity of its behavior over time is largely a reflection of the complexity of the environment in which it finds itself." Let us now turn to examine a special element of the environment in which man finds himself, a feature we must understand if we are to understand how genetic restrictions on cooperative social behavior with non-closely related conspecifics have been transcended significantly for the first time.[25]

Not only is the physical or organic environmental ecosystem of an organism full of "information" with which genetic information interacts and becomes coadapted, but there is a special division of man's environment which is structured by "culture" in the anthropologic sense of that term. Human culture is so packed with necessary information for life that the gene pool of *Homo* must have become inviable apart from it at least as far back as when we became dependent on the social transmission of hunting-and-gathering lore and technologies. Our underlying genetic library of information for living—which is selected from, stored in, and transmitted through genotypes within the genetic information pool of the species—obviously has been *fit* in the temporal dimension (the primary biological meaning of "fit") to keep us adapted or persisting in being over a very long time. It is also *fit* in the dimension of environmental range and complexity to enlarge the range and complexity of ecological niches we could occupy during the past thousand million years. But our fitness in both these dimensions, especially the latter, has been enhanced increasingly in the past one million years by our new cultural library of information for living—which is selected from, stored in, and transmitted through brains (often aided by brain-created artifacts external to our organisms, including books) in the cultural information pool of our species. The cultural information has become increasingly essential for the life of our species as this information has adapted us increasingly to ecological niches to which we are not and even could not be adapted by genetic information alone, even if the rate of genetic selection could be increased more than a thousandfold to catch up with the rate of cultural selection.

Cultural "information" indeed is stored in the brains of the population at the points where the genetic and the novel neurological memory of somatic learning overlap. The human brain is the integrating mechanism within which three levels of nature are coadapted to produce human nature. I presented in 1951 to an early meeting of the Society for the Scientific Study of Religion this trinity of the information that shapes human behavior. The trinity consists of (1) the physical elements of our environment, (2) the genotype, and (3) the culturetype.[26] It seemed to me then that the empirical data for understanding human nature in its deeper dimensions required an understanding of the presence of and relation among these three very different but interacting levels of our nature and required that we recognize the temporal and causal sequence or emergence of these three levels of structures in our development.

The relation between the human gene pool and the prehuman habitat—and the reciprocity of the two systems of information—at that time already was beginning to become clear from the neo-Darwinian evolutionary pictures presented by such as Julian Huxley and George Gaylord Simpson, although the term "information" in its new scientific meanings was not yet being used. We are presently at a similar or perhaps somewhat earlier stage in our understanding of the joint or reciprocal interactions between the culturetype and the other two systems. As recently as 1961, anthropologists generally shunned notions of cultural evolution and particularly the notion of any transhuman natural selection (genetic or nongenetic) operating in it. The proposals from outside the social sciences by men like Huxley, Simpson, and Theodosius Dobzhansky have been a powerful influence in opening our intellectual horizons to the interaction between these levels.[27]

The Societal Organism as a New "Creature" with which Sapiens is Symbiotic

With the enlarged view of human evolution presented above, we can continue with our picture of the mechanism by which genetically selfish humans become social cooperators by a symbiotic adaptation to a new creature, the *societal organism,* that has relatively recently emerged in the evolution of genetic man's ecological niche.

While the thrust of *Homo sapiens* into an entirely unprecedented success as a social animal has been noted clearly by Campbell and others in this issue of *Zygon,* as well as by Wilson in his *Sociobiology* and many others,[28] I do not find that anyone has yet provided an adequate explanation of how human evolution overcame the prohibition of cooperation between the competing genetic lines so clearly presented by Williams and others and generally acknowledged in biology. The hypothesis that I advance is that this prohibition has been transcended specifically by *Homo*'s adaptation in symbiosis with what is tantamount to a new kind of living creature in its environment. Humanity is not a single species but a new kind of symbiotic community. While there are many other biological species, such as grains and cattle, in the human ecological community, these are of secondary significance for human society and would not make human society significantly different in character from insect societies. The significant symbiosis of *Homo* is with a new creature such as the earth had never seen before, a creature that is only partly biological, only partly programmed by genetic information. In this symbiosis between biological men and sociocultural systems, men are in a sense analogous to the species of flagellate protozoa that became symbiotically adapted to serve a function in the intestine of termites in return for reciprocal advantages. But the new being or "creature" within which men are symbiotic is a societal organism, the critically significant elements of whose being are not only not programmed by anything in the human gene pool but not programmed by any gene pool whatsoever. The evolution of culture is postgenetic or a new kind of epigenetic information produced by the nongenetic selection of brain patterns.

The two systems of this symbiosis, men and sociocultural organisms, are as entwined and interdependent in their operations as are some of the paired but basically independent and originally separate elements that constitute the dynamic interactions that we call biological systems—such as the chromosomal nucleus and the cytoplasmic DNA of the mitochondria of a cell or as the metazoan zygote and the epigenetic information source that interacts with it to differentiate the successive generations of the zygote to form a complex organism—so that the semi-independence and distinction in the heredity-transmission processes are difficult to untangle. But to understand human social cooperation it is necessary to disentangle them and to show that the societal organism is indeed an independent living creature to which biological man is symbiotically adapted to constitute humanity. I shall seek to show the *independence* of animal man and sociocultural system and the *living* character of the latter as the newly emergent symbiotic partner of organic man; but first I want to emphasize humanity as the name of the symbiotic community. Emerson early called his symbiotic termite communities supraorganisms—those complex, coadapted, cooperating communities of species that function together in the ecosystems associated with termite nests in a coordinate way as in an organism.

Wilson's *Sociobiology* presents a good account of what biologists have called superorganisms in his account (in chaps. 18 and 19) of the first of four pinnacles of social evolution: the colonial invertebrates (including the corals, the jellyfish-like siphonophores, and others). Wilson has pointed out that this first peak in social evolution was the most successful in terms of cohesiveness, altruism, and cooperativeness—except possibly for the fourth pinnacle, which is human society. According to Wilson, the possibilities of social cooperation appear to diminish as the unit organisms get more elaborate, as we see in his evolutionary sequence of the first three pinnacles running from (1) the remarkably organism-like zooids of the primitive colonial invertebrates (that can make up such a complex, organism-like structure as the Portuguese man-of-war), where each colony starts from a single zygote and hence possesses a genetic relation of 1; through (2) the societies made up of such complex individuals as the ants or termites, where the genetic relation is commonly $\frac{1}{2}$ to $\frac{3}{4}$; to (3) the weakly social mammals, such as lions or monkeys, where the genetic relation among siblings cannot average more than $\frac{1}{2}$ and where decreasing relation seems to mean decreasing degrees of cooperation. The social bonds and specialization of functions are so weak in mammals prior to man that there is little tendency to see any resemblance to a superorganism as there was in the siphonophores. I emphasize that the decreasing degree of cooperation in this series of three stages parallels the decrease in their genetic relatedness.

I call attention to the fact, important for solving our problem, that in the evolution of life prior to, developing along
with, and fundamental for all these four pinnacles there were
two other stages essential for social bonding and cooperative
behavior.

One stage was the metazoon or the true organism—a society
composed of many cells, such as is the case for all higher
species of plant and animal organisms. Here, overcoming the
genetic prohibition of even self-sacrificial cooperation was
possible because all the cells of the organism were and are
programmed in fact by identical genotypes—added to which
the overwhelming majority of the population of cells in an
organism are genetically sterile and not, therefore, in competition. Even though the metazoa achieved extremely loyal services and unhesitating altruistic self-sacrifice of cells on behalf
of the well-being of their social organism, they also maintained
the genetic variability—necessary for continued evolution by
selection—in a specially segregated operation for the propagation of their species. This is a dual wisdom to be kept in mind
by human social planners of cultural patterns. The segregation
of the function of transmitting the varied genetic potentialities
is related to the other stage.

The other stage was the emergence of sex, of bisexual
reproduction, which required the cooperation of a male and a
female organism each significantly genetically different from
the other. In this adaptation, natural selection found a way to
elicit at least a temporary cooperative act, copulation, from two
creatures whose genetic blueprints indeed were competing
within the same species. It was highly adaptive (for any species
possessed of sufficient diversity in its gene pool that had
already been tested as reasonably viable) in providing useful
genetic variation for more readily meeting changing environmental contingencies at a much reduced cost as compared with
producing variability by mutation. Providing variability by
sexual recombination was possible because of the emergence
earlier of the dual strands of genetic information for maintaining life systems, a dual strand necessitated by somatic death
and genetic reproduction.

From primitive sexuality emerged what we know in mammalian and human life as the family. From the highly adaptive

virtues of sexual recombination of genes there would naturally be strong selection for powerful mechanisms to insure mating regardless of obstacles of any kind, including those inherent in genetics. The powerful sex bond between parents and the mutual kinship bonds to and among their offspring provide explanation for the motivation of high levels of cooperation and even self-sacrifice in families. From the combination of the powerful sex bonds and close-kin ties of families and extended families there emerged the possibility of motivation for social cooperation among creatures with moderately diverse genotypes. Sexual and kinship bonds are probably essential pillars of human society. I believe we now can begin to explain how and why the often unnatural and unwanted (so far as instinctive motivations are concerned) taboos or restraints concerning sexual behavior in human society were selected in cultural evolution as good or desirable and have been rein-forced by rituals, myths, and more direct social constraints: simply because sex privileges and kinship bonds are of the essence in shaping the motivations for social cooperation. The family and sexual bond and related strategies are a foundation on which the fourth and most unique and successful of Wilson's pinnacles of social evolution—human society—was erected at the motivational level.

Human society is the first vertebrate society significantly larger than sexual partners and offspring where conspecific organisms of widely diverse genotypes have become socially organized into anything like the complexity of interdependent, organic functioning that excels that of the social insects and in some ways even that of the colonial invertebrates. The colonial invertebrates were all colonies where each cell had the same genetic blueprint, except for possibly a very interesting case, that H. Oka reports finding in one of the tunicate colonies, with a "recognition gene" which, acting analogously to the mechan-ism for sexual recombination, permits two colonies to combine without the usual rejection and necrosis responses that usually prohibit cooperation between cells or organisms with different genotypes.[29] Human societies have extended cooperative moti-vation generally to include genetically diverse conspecifics by means of neurologically mediated cultural "recognition genes," a sociocultural mechanism analogous to the biogenetic mechanisms that have shaped bisexual reproduction and the family.

But the new evolutionary emergent in mankind is an even more radical one than the emergence of sex and the family into kin-group societies. This should be clear from the fact that within populations whose genes are competing there is little or no evidence of elaborate social organization approaching that of an "organism" or "supraorganism" beyond the bounds of close family ties until man arrived.

Central for an effective theory or explanation of the emergence and continued existence of stable, cooperatively functioning communities of conspecific organisms, most of whose alternative genetic forms are competing under natural selection, is a demonstration that the whole population indeed is patterned genetically to be adapted symbiotically to a common, external, or extraspecific living creature. And even here the symbiosis must provide advantages for continuation of a genetic line that are greater than the advantages conferred by competition with conspecific organisms. (I shall leave to another place the problem and solution of *Homo*'s need for continued genetic competition.)

My hypothesis—that human sociocultural systems are indeed such external or independent living creatures, truly societal "organisms"—might imply that I am following a tradition advanced by such men as Auguste Comte and Herbert Spencer. But my concept arose in fact from a different direction and has the advantage of being formulated in the light of the contemporary understandings of evolutionary mechanisms that I outlined above. We are forced to develop some such hypothesis by the conjunction of such clear evidence as Williams presents for the nonselection of altruism by competing alleles, combined with the clear evidence that in man the empirical fact is we do have a unique case of non-kin societies with high degrees of cooperation. Moreover, the new extensions of evolutionary theory now allow a credible hypothesis. Campbell's suggestions on how this fits in with facts of sociocultural evolution and how religions have provided the motivating mechanisms for overcoming our genetically programmed selfishness have greatly aided me in developing my hypothesis to resolve the problem of cultural evolution.

The primary problem is to show how a body of life-shaping information is established and transmitted independently of the human gene pool and how it shapes a behaving or living system in ways unspecified by the human gene pool but instead has evolved or been selected as symbiotically adapted to populations of wide ranges of human phenotypes and their correlated genotypes. This is not difficult in the light of recent biological theory and data.

The Independence of Societal Organisms from Particular Populations of Homo

The generating heritage of the "societal organisms" with which populations of *Homo* have become symbiotic is quite separate from heritages generating plants and animals. To be sure, man lives in interdependent symbiosis with such creatures as cows or pigs and wheat or corn, just as the flagellates live in symbiosis with the termite. All the prehuman species in such an ecological community are programmed for such cooperative or mutual functioning by genotypes dealt out more or less randomly from the gene pools of the respective species, and those that are adapted are selected. The same is true for the elaborate societies of insects within their elaborate ecological communities of interdependent flora and fauna. But the human societal organism is programmed only partially by the human gene pool. It is a creature in whose evolution its informational sources, although highly specific, have become increasingly nongenic or epigenetic and not specified by the DNA of the chromosomes. Its phenotype or body is, of course, a population of human bodies of diverse genetic heritages, together with various culture-specific societal artifacts. The societal organisms, like Emerson's supraorganisms, also include in their "somata" a number of nonhuman organisms, including those found on farms. Such societal organisms are structured by the combined information transmitted as culture and the genetic information carried in the gene pools of all the symbiotic plants and animals as well as the diversified genotypes of *Homo*.

I have followed Williams, Wilson, and others in specifying that the societal organism is made possible only by the evolution of a complex brain. The new "gonad" or information storehouse for the phylogeny of the societal organism is the collectivity of somatic cells found in a population of human brains. This collectivity has the capacity to receive and transmit symbols that are determinative of behavior of a changing population of brains. To a remarkable degree it is independent of what particular sampling of the human gene pool provides the basic structures of those brains. This possibility has emerged in the coadaptation of the social organism in symbiosis with *H. sapiens. Sapiens'* brains were selected genetically by the circumstances of evolving symbiosis in an environment created by the societal organism so as to provide the complex powers for understanding and communicating the possibilities of adaptive advantages for each individual *sapiens* in return for his symbiotic services to the societal organism.

One of the essential coadaptations of the human gene pool was the loose coupling already referred to above between the reptilian level of the human brain (with its tightly genetically controlled response patterns) and the new outer cortex (with its capacities for receiving, remembering, and transmitting the heritage of a societal organism). As already pointed out, the societal organism in fact has no other "gonad" than the human brain, even though much of its culturetype (the analogue of the genotype) and consequently much of the phenotype lie outside the biological organisms of *Homo* in all kinds of artifacts—such as tools, hearths, pots, gardens, houses, shrines, tablets, cities, maps, ships, books, blueprints, buggies, roads, factories, metropolitan complexes—to which the symbiont *sapiens* swarm both to service and to utilize. But, without a living brain produced by the gene pool of *Homo*, no ritual traditions, myths, or printed books are generated, communicated, and responded to. One exception is some recently emerged artifacts, the computer-operated cybernetic systems—primitive, new, almost living creatures that possibly may become symbiotic with *Homo* and his symbiotic societal organism and eventually replace both of them.[30]

The specimens of Humanity—societal organisms in symbiosis with biological organisms—are huge, supraorganismic "phenotypes," consisting of a population of genetically diverse individual human phenotypes, many nonhuman species, and include an elaborate, extrasomatic, artifactual apparatus. I shall be inclined to use the single creature, the "societal organism," to denote the symbiotic union of societal organism and the population of *sapiens* that constitutes the local ecosystemic supraorganic phenotype of Humanity, just as for biologists the much larger and visible "termite" is used to denote a similar symbiosis of one very large individual of one species with many thousands of the tiny individuals of the symbiotic species inside it, even though a proper analysis requires recognition of the two genetically independent species whose symbiosis generates the "phenotype."

The bonds that bind the genetically diverse ape-men with the supraorganism are the neurologically transmitted promises of greater benefits from symbiosis with a societal organism whose life is long and faithful compared to men. Some of them have a continuity of thousands of years, as in Egypt. Like biological organisms, societal organisms are composed of parts or "organs" such as a language or an agricultural, mining, manufacturing, or transportational technology. Unlike biological organisms, because of the Lamarckian heredity mechanisms of brains, these parts are more readily transplantable from one societal organism to another and are known to persist as transplants in evolving continuity for thousands of years. Societal organisms are thus modifiable and can evolve, in Lamarckian fashion without death, by recombinations of information in a multitude of ways. In a 1960 discussion of how the societal organism evolved Henry Alexander Murray in puckish analogy with "gene" suggested it would be by mutations of "idenes."[31]

The Independence and Coadaptation of the Genotypic and Culturetypic Heritages of Humanity

The viability of a societal organism depends upon its own transmission of the essential information to structure the behavior of the symbiotic collectivity in such ways that reciprocal gains indeed are experienced by the participating individuals. The selection of the *Homo*–societal organism symbiosis is a two-way adaptation, as in the case of the coadapted genetic pools of flagellates and termites. But in the case of the societal organism there is only a partial genotype or gene pool for its own distinctive attributes, in contrast with the full genotype in the termite. This partial genetic structure is, of course, some segment of the human gene pool that produces the varied phenotypes that constitute the societal organism. Societal organisms are, as we well know, "parasites" on human individuals, just as human individuals are mutually parasitic upon their societal organisms. The great variety of the individual human phenotypes and corresponding genotypes within the societal organism is a part of the design that makes human societies so much richer than insect societies and supraorganisms. But, as we have seen, because such human populations cannot become organically or cooperatively organized by the genetic source, a special, epigenetic source of information has emerged. This portion of the generating information of the societal organism is its culturetype. This information is stored in the brains and correlated artifacts of the collectivity of the diverse phenotypes of *H. sapiens* constituting a societal organism.

In each case, the information structuring each type or "species" of societal organism, which I have called "culturetype" more commonly than "idenotype" (and hence I was interested just recently to learn that Boyd and Richerson independently have used the same term),[32] has to be adapted to each *sapiens* phenotype and hence is selected by (or made "fit" with respect to) the particularity of each *sapiens* genotype on the average (no matter how varied they may be) within the human population embraced by the societal organism.

It is commonly observable that, when this adaptation does not take place, either the unfit societal organism or a number of its unfit individual persons are "selected out" by the nature of the situation. To some degree societal organisms can immunize themselves from destructive or cancerous deviants (whether the deviation is genetic or learned does not matter) by various systems of ostracism, ejection, immunization, or incarceration. But the very nature of symbiosis implies that, for the statistical average and indeed for the vast majority of any viable cases, the adaptation has been suitably engendered internally in the basic motivational mechanisms of each of the parties to the symbiosis.

The societal organism is as transcendent to all creatures in

the biological kingdoms as those biological creatures are transcendent to the prebiological, chemical coacervate species in the
tidal pools before there evolved the symbiosis of amino with
nucleic acid polymers to constitute a biological cell. In the past
million years—or perhaps in only the past ten thousand years,
as far as urban civilization is concerned—mankind has been
witnessing and participating in an event that is without equal in
the evolution of life since about a billion years ago. What has
happened is the emergence in the human brain of a new
memory system for phylogenetic information which is essentially independent of a particular gene pool and yet coadapted
to it in a "symbiotic" relation of mutual benefits. John Kendrew pointed out:

We may thus describe three different types of information that are of
importance in biological systems: [1] the genetic information, which does not
[during a lifetime] have feedback from the organisms but is passed on from
generation to generation; [2] stored sense data [in the brain], which do have
considerable feedback into the storage system of the organisms but are not
passed down [like the genes] from generation to generation; and finally [3]
communicated data, which do have feedback and are also passed down to the
next generation. It is the possession of the third kind of information in large
amounts that makes *Homo sapiens* unique as a species; . . .[33]

It is this cultural information that informs, shapes, or structures the human societal organism as a totality and does this
independently (beyond a certain point) of most of the details of
the genetic base of information that shapes the characteristics
of the societal organism's constituent human individuals. Julian
Huxley sensed this. Man, this unique kind of animal, had
crossed "a threshold to a new kind of phase of evolution, which
may be called 'cultural' or 'human' or 'psychosocial.' " The late
geneticist H. J. Muller had somewhat related views.[34] This does
not mean that genetic evolution is over or no longer necessary.
On the contrary, genetic selection is just as essential as ever it
was, and it will need to become a part of our future ethics if we
are to survive, as Muller emphasizes. In my hypothesis of
symbiotic coadaptation of genetic and cultural information it is
essential that our cultural wisdom "satisfy" the prior requirements inherent in the variety of genotypes that shape the
phenotypes of the societal organism's human population.
Insofar as a complex hierarchy of systems (such as a civilization

or an ecosystem) have been coadapted to constitute a more or less integrated whole to perform a set of integrated functions in which the several subsystems are essential participants, it is logically inescapable then that no essential part, element, or species in the system can be hurt without hurting the whole. Hence in the societal organism there has to be a cybernetic control system to provide what Emerson has called "dynamic homeostasis."[35] Each part has to be kept in mutually optimal "symbiotic" adaptation to all other parts. Just as the symbiotic termite and flagellate species are mutually adapted to make a viable or stable organic community and ecological niche, so the populations of the animal species *sapiens* and the various kinds of its symbiotic societal organisms must be adapted to each other. This point is of the essence. Neither one can be wholly independent or disregarding of the other, or the symbiosis will be harmed, just as is the case for the parties to any of the ecological symbioses.

It has been noted by anthropologists and historians that there are societies that have failed or have been eliminated. In some cases the errors were mismatches between the sociocultural information (culturetypes) and the variety of human genotypes in the gene pool. In other cases the errors were mismatches between the culturetypes of the societal organisms and the larger ecosystem, including other societal organisms. In some cases certain populations of phenotypes (and their further contribution to the gene pool) have been wiped out completely by starvation, disease, or war, thus changing the character of (selecting) the genetic and cultural pools of humanity. This is one mechanism by which Wilson's and Simpson's earlier suggestions for the continuing matching of the genetic with the sociocultural information to achieve a common viable phenotype may be carried out. One can say that the selection processes that simultaneously act upon the several sources of genetic and cultural information that combine to shape the symbiotic *sapiens* and the societal organism actually operate to coadapt the totality of information harbored and transmitted in each of these beings so as to be on the whole productive of the viability of this totality within the larger ecosystem of which it is a component.

One might note in passing a few of the advantages of the new symbiosis for rapid selection and evolution, as compared with the Mendelian genetic system by itself. As Wilson, Kendrew, and others have pointed out, the evolutionary rate of Mendelian populations requires at least a few generations, say of the order of ten, to make some small changes. For *Homo,* this means a few centuries at least. The new symbiosis of *Homo* with the societal organisms has allowed men in a few years to transcend by a millionfold the rate of the evolution of flight that took millions of years for such biological classes as Insecta and Aves. The evolution of aviation in the symbiotic *sapiens*–societal organism hardly has been going on for a century, and through it *Homo* has accomplished what no creature programmed only by selection of genes has or probably ever could bring about: a flight to the moon. The new culturetypes can leap from brain to brain and transform persons and culturetypes in split seconds and do this almost simultaneously for the world population of billions via telecommunications systems, as when a war starts or a new medical benefit is discovered. But our main question is exactly how the culturetype of a social organism binds a genetically diverse population into a highly cooperative, living whole or supraorganism.

The Coadaptation of Culturetypes with a Diverse Population of Human Genotypes: A Result of Religions

If we look into the locus of that portion of a societal organism's life-shaping information called culturetype, as we have noted, instead of being harbored in the gonads it is harbored in an organ at the other end of the spinal column of the vertebrate *Homo.* We also have noted that each individual brain is fed its basic and somewhat differing or unique values (goals) from its unique genotype, which programs the development of its structures and behavioral proclivities. We need to consider how the brain is at the same time the seat of the common culturetype. In optimally viable human societies my hypothesis would say that the culturetype is essentially identical (as are the genotypes of identical twins or of the cells of an organism) within all the brains of a population constituting a societal organism. The two sources of information in the brain give man his "two natures" that so often are not wholly mutually adapted. To the extent that these two natures fail to be completely harmonious, we find the tension so familiar to religious tradition and lamented by Saint Paul who complained of this conflict in his celebrated confession: "For I know that nothing good lodges in me—in my unspiritual nature, I mean—for though the will to do good is there, the deed is not. The good which I want to do, I fail to do; but what I do is the wrong which is against my will; clearly it is no longer I who am the agent, but sin that has its lodging in me. . . . Miserable creature that I am, who is there to rescue me out of this body doomed to death?"

Fortunately, the harmony between a population of *sapiens* and a societal organism is not always at such a discouraging level. Perhaps in most brains the consciousness of a possible disharmony between the two natures does not become very acute because of a genetically inbuilt buffer. The total system is probably too complex and insufficiently explored for a scientifically valid analysis at the moment, but it is exactly such tensions or pressures to adapt—whether genetically or socioculturally—that provide individual men and societal organisms with their phenomenally high rates of evolving. At the same time, protective mechanisms against cognitive and aesthetic dissonances that are too radical and too disruptive have been evolved by both genes and cultures. We cannot do without the wretched religious prophets and artistic perceivers of sin and evil. The whole system for social or ethical motivation of individual persons requires there to be in societal organisms the information necessary for their being adapted to the requirements of the wide diversity of the genotypes of individuals in the population on the one side and to the requirements of the larger ecosystem on the other.

A central societal agent in accomplishing this has been religion. Beginning as much as one hundred thousand years ago, according to estimates published by Dobzhansky and Anthony F. C. Wallace, religions evolved to meet these several sets of ultimate requirements as the central value core of the societal organisms. They have become intricately adapted to the wide spectrum of human genotypes (and hence phenotypes) out of which each society is itself constituted and also adapted to the total ecological community that is the niche of the societal organism. I shall summarize a few main points on which I and others have written more fully elsewhere.

Within any viable or adapted specimen of a societal organism, religions have been relatively coherent systems of information, transferred from brain to brain by ritual, myth, and theology (three successive levels of culturetypes or idenes). Because they have presented a common system of meaning communicated by ritual and myth of a particular tribal population symbolizing loyalty to common ancestors (family kinship) and to various common rights and duties enculturated from impressionable infancy and childhood on up to death, religions in culturetypes have functioned analogously to the common genotype that bonds the members of the primitive organic societies such as the social insects. As the number of families and the genetic range of the tribes and tribal associations increased, the rituals and myths came to celebrate ancestors and gods sufficiently remote and sovereign over all to maintain the family image and loyalties. In some cases at least, there were stories to celebrate the partial extension of the loyalty to more distantly related families through marriage. While such images could not provide the actual close genetic bonds such as those in the social insects, they could provide the equivalent benefit for all the genetic lines cooperating within ever larger tribal groups in what we may call "virtual" or "spiritual" brotherhood. This benefit came by virtue of any stray or alien person's symbiotic affiliation with one particular societal organism through a voluntary acceptance of its culturetype. This provided the common bonds that would insure a statistically better chance for the genetic line of any faithful adherent than would nonaffiliation. The reciprocal favors or cooperation within the societal organism insured this for individual man as did the protection of the termite's gut insure the viability of the symbiotic flagellates. At the basic level of analysis, Marx and Freud were wrong in debunking religions as false myths. While Freud was a pioneer in unveiling some aspects of myths, he presumably was not aware of what we now know concerning the prohibition of cooperation beyond the family by genetic mechanisms or the essential validity of the religious myths for transcending this.

The information which the religious segment of the culturetype transmits provides the cybernetic norms for the societal organism, shaping the roles and loyalties of all the adhering population (no matter how genetically diversified they became in some cases) to function in the service of the societal organism with the same efficacy as the flagellates serve the needs of the termite. But it should be noted that my hypothesis does not grant to humans the same degree of somatic self-sacrifice for the societal organisms that are possible for the social insects and individuals in the colonial microorganisms. There is nothing in the human situation that makes possible continued genetic fitness when the individual organism is sacrificed before giving rise to offspring. While in very close relatives, such as in the three-quarter to unity relationships found in social insects and colonial microorganisms, there can be sacrifice of somata while enhancing genetic fitness, this is not even theoretically possible in vertebrates. Hence the societal organism must be so programmed or informed that it actually does provide fitness, statistically at least, to each of the individual humans it admits to its organism. Hence religions have evolved to transmit values and motivations in their adhering populations that effectively result in the implied, long-term salvation of the soul beyond the death of the body. The soul, as I have written in other papers, includes the genetic information which does possess indeed the kind of immortality that religions long have proclaimed. I should note also that by "soul" I do not refer to the peculiar myths or theologies of any particular religion but to whatever may be translated scientifically as their analogue or equivalent for the continuity of life and true being, such as the karma-nirvana doctrines in Eastern religions.

Because the product of religious enculturation and the resulting societal behavior patterns does result in greater fitness statistically to the individuals involved, one could say that religions serve as "immunizing" agents for the body politic against the potential virulence of the inherently competing and hence alien genetic patterns within it. Except for close kin, each individual is competing genetically with the others within the society. Without any agency which provides the brain with information to neutralize or "immunize" the usual consequences of these genetic differences and to motivate the proper service roles, we could not have our unique kinds of societal organisms. Religions in fact must guarantee an effective coadaptation of the diverse individuals with the societal organism so as to produce at least as good a chance for the continuation of each individual's genetic line as would going it separately in some primitive primate kinship groups.

Religion and religious information in the form of rituals, myths, and theologies have been selected themselves in the evolution of our genotypes and culturetypes. Their evolution yields a "phylogenetic" sequence. Genetically programmed biological rituals originated perhaps more than a hundred million years ago. Culturally transmitted ritual patterns are evident in avian and mammalian species, indicating that these may have arisen in our ancestry at least ten million years ago. Oral myths tied to these rituals (which have been found by anthropologists in primitive societies rather generally) could not have arisen until the human brain had evolved the capacity for linguistic communication, which would date them not earlier than a few hundred thousand years ago. Consciously created logical clarifications and explanations of the myths—theologies—arose only in the past few thousand years after the emergence of writing and of extensive logical purification of linguistic symbols and the emergence of their successful use in logical calculations concerning the real world and its future.

In addition to Hoagland's generalization about brain function, which I cited above, there is a wealth of data accumulated by biologists and ethologists, psychologists and psychiatrists, and neurophysiologists and anthropologists to show the selective advantages that led to increasing ritual communication of information and hence increasing selection for the elaborations of the brain cortex in our ancestors during the past several million years, with a recent burst of sociocultural communication and evolution of culturetypes when the neocortex was selected for capacities in linguistic communication. Ritual communication was limited at first to signals sent in the form of bodily behaviors at the level of instincts. Often they were phylogenetically derived response patterns that evolved to become available for intra- and interspecies signals as conspecifics and other creatures evolved to respond to them adaptively. This communication was mediated by the reptilian level of the brain and connects very tightly with our genetic instructions. The power of religion to motivate behavior comes from its contact with the basic motivational mechanisms of our earliest and most basic or genetic nature.[36]

It should be kept in mind that the wealth of ritual communication that is so useful in maintaining our social relations—such as smiles, frowns, and growls—was genetically programmed behavior that had started to evolve more than a hundred million years ago and continued to evolve in our ancestors during the past few million years in the small anthropoidal kin-group societies. These genetically programmed, lower-brain patterns for ritual emitting and responding to messages from other individuals also were coadapted undoubtedly in more recent evolution with the capacities of our brains to handle the more abstract linguistic forms of communication and with the more complex forms of social life that slowly evolved over the past few hundred thousand years of our hunting and gathering ancestors and into the period when close-kin groups became more extended. The genetic information in this ritual-communication system still must be evolving in coadaptation with the complexities of modern civilizations wherever more viable coadapted symbioses of genetically and culturally transmitted information are being selected over others.

Linguistic communication evolved with new connections between the deeper, genetically more closely programmed layer of the brain and the outer layer where the genetic expression has been adapted to produce mechanisms for processing a more flexible, independent, and highly organized and complex system of symbols not transmitted through the genetic but only in the cultural pool. This bridging within the brain of information from the genotype with that from the culturetype by means of correlated internal associations of a set of words communicated between two or among two billion brains of widely diverse genetic heritage and also widely diverse nonlinguistic cultural heritage and individual experience gave fantastic new power to man. (Recently, picture books, photographs, motion pictures, and television have been providing a similar revolution for another important channel of communication of meaning developed in another part of the brain—the associations of nonlinguistic visual and sonic patterns that present meanings.) The internal associations of verbal stimuli upon the brain ever retain their connectibility to the basic ritual signals and response patterns, to the deepest emotional feelings and motivations. At the same time the same sets of words are capable of the most refined elaborations of complex meanings of both great literature and abstract science. Hence the brain of any individual becomes the house for a culturetype held in common with a community of other brains inhabiting a societal organism as well as the house of its own unique genetic character and personal experience. Through linguistically transmitted stories or myths elaborated in a long-living societal organism involving thousands or millions of other brains both ancestral and now living, the individual became simultaneously a creature of his genotype and a creature of his culturetype.

Within the past few thousand years, man's linguistic capacities evolved by the selection of the most viable patterns of the phenotypic expressions of the variations of genotypes and culturetypes, the dual sources of information shaping the behavior of individuals and their societal-organism hosts. Writing emerged to hold verbal forms and associations in stable patterns outside human brains. By 600 B.C. linguistic symbols emerged as so powerful logically that philosophy, geometry, and theology began to flourish, to be followed within a couple of thousand years by modern science, the most phenomenal explosion of information thus far in the history of the earth, pointing to an as yet incipient scientific theology and world-wide religion.

At all levels of the complex symbiotic development of men and societal systems, each adapted to the other in ways that were mutually beneficial as the religious rituals, myths, and theologies evolved to represent progressive, adaptive programs.

Religion early gave correct recognition to the new nature of man. As I have noted, Saint Paul in his classical letters distinguished man's higher spiritual nature (which seems to be related to the aspect of the brain that is informed by the culturetype) from his bodily nature (related to the aspect of the brain informed by the genotype). Insofar as a brain is informed by a culturetype which is well integrated with its genotypic information, then that brain actually incarnates and provides means for the expression of a large fraction of the central values of the total culturetype as well as expresses that brain's particular genotype. The self-consciousness as well as the unconscious phenomena of that brain may be said, in a biological analogy, to be converted into a culturally "identical twin" with all other similarly culturally coadapted brains. Hence it is closer than a merely biological brother to all other brains in the sociocultural system (societal organism) and thus is spiritually (by culturetype) united with the total population of its particular society. To the extent that the genetic program indeed is coadapted with that particular culturetype, then the individual's social and private responsibilities become joined as one, and the individual finds elation in his oneness with all his human spiritual brothers who have become closer than genetic brothers, insofar as his culturetype is identical with that of his fellowmen in a societal organism. The properly enculturated, individual, adult brain becomes the source of consciousness or self-awareness of a new being, transcending its immediate organic body. In this analysis of the evolving material systems that constitute Humanity, we can see that such a consciousness reflects the scientifically described reality involved.

Insofar as the genotypic-culturetypic symbiosis is also well adapted to the total ecosystem, which is the new being's habitat (adaptation to which is the source of life for the new being), the conscious spirit of man is one with all creation. Brains, as coordinating centers of the multiple agencies for adapting, are programmed genetically and culturally to respond to a recognition of such an adaptation to the total ecosystem by producing an experience of ecstasy followed by a high level of spiritual satisfaction and motivation. Peace, new meaning, moral courage, hope, and related religious experiences or feelings naturally arise whenever the frustrations of a bodily self-centeredness are transformed to a vision of the higher self which transcends the body. These feelings remain or are restored whenever that vision is revalidated in experience.

It is toward the goal of union with or adaptation to the total system of powers shaping man's natural habitat (always including primarily one's fellow human beings involved in the societal organism with which he is symbiotic) that it has been the function of religions to motivate and sustain human beings.

Revitalization of Religious Truth on the Level with Science

In the past few centuries, for increasing numbers of people and societal organisms, there has been a loss in the efficacy of their religions because, for the most part, the religious myths or their more developed theologies (where these had emerged) became disjoined from and incredible among the new sciences. When religion once again becomes updated to constitute a credible vision of an individual's ties with his society and his cosmos, it again will deliver us from our alienation and meaninglessness and engender the cooperative or moral dispositions essential to the coadaptation of the individual *sapiens* symbionts with their societal organism. Although Saint Paul did not have the details that we now have concerning man's two natures and their relation to total nature, our scientific perspective seems to confirm his general analysis and—with some slight corrections and translations to modern equivalents—also his answer to the question of who will deliver me from this body of sin and death.[37]

I immediately must note, however, an important point from the modern scientific picture that transcends in clarity and credibility anything I know of in previous theology. The human spirit (and conscious mind), while indeed a reflection of the body-transcending information of the culturetype whose enculturation in our brain renders us one with our local society and ecosystem, still is primarily dependent upon its genetic information, without which no human individuals or societies of any kind could exist. The human soul and its salvation involve genes as well as idenes. This should help to clear me of any theological charges of gnosticism.

This brings me back to genetics. In order to attract and hold any individual human symbionts to constitute its incarnation, the first requirement of any societal organism's culturetype is that it promise and deliver greater longevity to the average if not to the bulk of the diverse types of genetic lines assemblable from its gene pool than would be probable from any competing societal organism or ecological niche. In other words, man's immortal substance is of the earth, earthy. The genes are as essential a part as the culture. The significant core or soul of human nature is a phenotypic reality created by the union of three distinct and enduring if not immortal heritages of information that have been coadapted by a selective process. The first is the "information" that structures the stable patterns of our earthly habitat. The second is the information in the gene pool, coadapted with or reflecting that of the physical habitat, which, in the context of the habitat, engenders biological organisms and ecosystems. The third, coadapted with the previous two, is our heritage of culturetypic information, which, in the context of the previous two, engenders human societies, civilizations, and ecosystems.

It is on the basis of the evolutionary role of religion that I have made my prophecy of its revitalization in a new stage of cultural evolution. In that stage theology no longer will be the deceased queen of the Greco-Roman heritage of the scientiae of the medieval period but will become the living queen, resurrected by new interpretations in the light of modern sciences—queen not because she is the primary source of truth but queen because she is the application of truth to the matters that are of primary significance or ultimate concern to men.

In "Natural Selection and God" and related papers I took "natural selection" and "God" quite seriously in their own cultural contexts and sought to translate between scientific and religious language to show what I considered to be their essentially analogous meanings.[38] The Jesuit Father Pierre Teilhard de Chardin, as a paleontologist, earlier had felt an equivalence between our evolutionary understanding of the creation and sustenance of man and the traditional religious and theological efforts to represent man's state in the scheme of things. While no individual or group has yet come up with a formulation completely acceptable in all points to the majorities in either the religious or the scientific communities, it seems clear that both communities concur that, while, in order to remain in being, man himself must cooperate actively in the program of creative evolution, in the end it is a system of creative power far transcending man that determines man's destiny, a self-creating selective system which has endowed man with the desire to cooperate with or adapt to it. It seems clear from the scientific pictures that man's chief end is to seek the requirements of the ultimate reality system and adapt to them—at least if he wants to continue as a body-transcending or body-transforming being on the outer envelope of the evolving systems of life on earth.

While, in present Western culture, the religious images or models of man's immortal nature and purpose largely have been dismissed, I have sought to show how information from various scientific disciplines is building up a picture of the immortal or "spiritual" realities at the core of *Homo's* phenotype, including those of which he is unconscious as well as those of which he is aware.

Without going into an analysis of the relation between conscious and unconscious elements of reality,[39] I would suggest here that the evolution of human consciousness—the production of awareness of relations among elements of self and the world—is a product of the symbiotic action of genotype and culturetype interacting with cosmotypes (the recurrent patterns of the human habitat) in shaping the brain and its behavior. Consciousness is a reflected image of creation. It is a product of a particular brain's internal behavior in its dynamic play with the system of symbols and mechanisms or strategies for playing that it has inherited and is currently being fed in the game of the continuing creation of life. In general the consciousness produced by the brain reflects or shows only that portion of the phenotype's present situation and potential activities that are likely to be most important for immediate decisions to enhance life. With varying amounts and urgencies of messages before it, consciousness is a judging or selecting mechanism, a temporary and local teleonomic agent empowered by and subject to the wisdom for life already donated to and accumulated in a particular brain. Conscious intent or purpose becomes teleological whenever it discovers "what" will be selected in the future by the fact that "what" is a potential stable state of the self in the future under new conditions offered by the universe.

This is the teleology to which I already have referred as so eloquently expressed by Bronowski in his picture of our universe as containing hidden preferences that chance or random variations sooner or later discover and bring into being as new levels of stability. Unfortunately, Jacques Monod and many others passed away before recognizing what Bronowski recognized a few years before: "There is therefore a peculiar irony in the vitalist claim that *the progress of evolution from simple to complex* cannot be the work of chance. On the contrary, as we see, exactly this *is how chance works, and is constrained to work by its nature.* The total potential stability that is hidden in matter can only be evoked in steps, each higher layer resting on the layer below it. The stable units that compose one layer are the raw material for random encounters which will produce higher configurations, some of which will chance to be stable. So long as there remains a potential of stability which has not become actual, there is no other way for chance to go."[40] This is similar to pictures presented by Simon, George Wald, and a number of others concerning the evolutionary process of the world.[41]

That the nature that selects in this expanded picture of natural selection is very much like some of the traditional gods, as far as man's proper aspirations and duties are concerned, seems increasingly clear. That such a nature or god demands and in fact insists on individual man's cooperative service to and union with his fellow man and with the requirements of the ultimate nature of reality (which is a proper translation of God) is another name for the whole picture of evolution: adaptation.

NOTES

1. Herbert A. Simon, "The Architecture of Complexity," *Proceedings of the American Philosophical Society* 106 (1962): 467-82 (reprinted in his *The Sciences of the Artificial* [Cambridge, Mass.: M.I.T. Press, 1969]); Howard H. Pattee, ed., *Hierarchy Theory: The Challenge of Complex Systems* (New York: George Braziller, Inc., 1973).

2. J. Bronowski, "New Concepts in the Evolution of Complexity: Stratified Stability and Unbounded Plans," *Zygon* 5 (1970): 18–35; Ralph Wendell Burhoe, "The Control of Behavior: Human and Environmental," *Journal of Environmental Health* 35 (1972): 247–58; idem, "The Civilization of the Future: Ideals and Possibility," *Philosophy Forum* 13 (1973): 149–77; idem, "The Human Prospect and the 'Lord of History,'" *Zygon* 10 (1975): 299–375.

3. B. F. Skinner, "The Phylogeny and Ontogeny of Behavior," *Science* 153 (1966): 1205–13.

4. Donald T. Campbell, "On the Conflicts between Biological and Social Evolution and between Psychology and Moral Tradition," in *American Psychologist* (December 1975), pp. 1103–26 and in *Zygon* 11 (1976): 167-208.

5. See my "Human Prospect," p. 326.

6. R. W. Sperry, "Science and the Problem of Values," *Zygon* 9 (1974): 7–21.

7. E. O. Wilson, *Sociobiology: The New Synthesis* (Cambridge, Mass.: Harvard University Press, Belknap Press, 1975); cf. e.g., pp. 159, 575.

8. Hudson Hoagland, "The Brain and Crises in Human Values," *Zygon* 1 (1966): 140–57.

9. The literature is large, complex, and unfinished, but a good introduction is Konrad Lorenz's *On Aggression* (New York: Harcourt, Brace & World, 1966), and, for moral development, see Lawrence Kohlberg, "Indoctrination versus Relativity in Value Education," *Zygon* 6 (1971): 285–310. In my "Human Prospect," in the section "Ancient Biological Roots of Religion," pp. 304–12, I gave a different treatment and cited several workers in the field. George Edgin Pugh has described the role of the brain in human decision systems in "Human Values, Free Will, and the Conscious Mind," *Zygon* 11 (1976): 2–24. A larger treatment of human values appears in his *On the Origin of Human Values* (New York: Basic Books, 1976) and provides many details that parallel my own development of this field.

10. Paul D. MacLean, "The Brain's Generation Gap: Some Human Implications," *Zygon* 8 (1973): 113–27.

11. Ibid., p. 120.

12. George C. Williams, *Adaptation and Natural Selection* (Princeton, N.J.: Princeton University Press, 1966), p. 95. For Wilson, see n. 7 above.

13. Campbell.

14. See n. 12 above, p. 93.

15. Ibid.

16. Ibid., p. 121.

17. Ralph Wendell Burhoe, "Natural Selection and God," *Zygon* 7 (1972): 30–63, or chap. 4 in this book.

18. Williams, p. 94. Robert L. Trivers's development is found in his "The Evolution of Reciprocal Altruism," *Quarterly Review of Biology* 46 (1971): 35–37.

19. I am greatly indebted to Emerson's "Dynamic Homeostasis: A Unifying Principle in Organic, Social, and Ethical Evolution," *Scientific Monthly* 78 (1954): 67–85 (reprinted with some revision in *Zygon* 3 [1968]: 129–68).

20. Alfred E. Emerson, "Ecology, Evolution and Society," *American Naturalist* 77 (1943): 117–18. He presents a more recent summary of "Reciprocal Phylogeny of Host Rhinotermitidae and Associated Organisms" including a section on "Evolution of Ecosystems" in his "Tertiary Fossil Species of the Rhinotermitidae (Isoptera), Phylogeny of Genera, and Reciprocal Phylogeny of Associated Flagellata (Protozoa) and the Staphylinidae (Coleoptera)," *Bulletin of the American Museum of Natural History* 146 (1971): 245–303. Two more readily accessible papers by Emerson provide details on population systems, intraspecies supraorganisms, and interspecies ecological supraorganisms, etc.: (1) his chaps. 24 and 33–35 in W. C. Allee et al., *Principles of Animal Ecology* (Philadelphia: W. B. Saunders Co., 1949) and (2) his "The Evolution of Adaptation in Population Systems," in *The Evolution of Life,* Evolution after Darwin: University of Chicago Centennial, 3 vols., ed. Sol Tax (Chicago: University of Chicago Press, 1960), 1:307–48. Incidentally, the three volumes in the series contain many papers pertinent to the proposals I am making concerning the relation of genetic and cultural evolution.

21. Williams, chap. 4, esp. p. 97.

22. For genetic selection as one of many mechanisms involved in stabilizing (remembering, maintaining, and reproducing) the patterns of life, see, for instance, John H. Holland, *Adaptation in Natural and Artificial Systems* (Ann Arbor: University of Michigan Press, 1975), or Simon's *Sciences of the Artificial* (n. 1 above). For living systems as guided patterns of energy flow, see, for instance, A. Katchalsky, "Thermodynamics of Flow and Biological Organization," *Zygon* 6 (1971): 99–125.

23. Howard T. Odum, *Environment, Power, and Society* (New York: Wiley-Interscience, 1971).

24. Bronowski (n. 2 above), pp. 30–31. See also my note at the bottom of p. 39 of my "Commentary" on Bronowski's paper, which he insisted I publish with it (*Zygon* 5 [1970]: 36–40): "Bronowski, in his concept of 'stratified stability,' has at last given a neat physical formulation that underlies all levels of the selective or adaptive process in evolution from atoms to human cultural patterns."

25. I was reminded of the extrachromosomal information in eucaryotic cells found in mitochondria, plastids, etc., by Emerson in a personal communication, expressing the view that some recent evidence was indicating that such cells were indeed symbiotic ecosystems akin to the views I am developing in this paper. I am not yet familiar with the literature of this field, although in an unpublished paper I have cited John C. Kendrew's brief remarks on it found on p. 193 of his paper cited in n. 33 below. The role or hierarchy is set forth in the papers edited by Howard H. Pattee (see n. 1 above). The quotation from Simon is from his *Sciences of the Artificial,* pp. 23–24.

26. Unpublished ms.; but see p. 364 of my "Human Prospect" for a review, and the whole paper for a certain development of the theme.

27. For a picture of the reemergence of notions of cultural evolution, see, for instance, Hudson Hoagland and Ralph Wendell Burhoe, eds., *Evolution and Man's Progress* (New York: Columbia University Press, 1962). Also, see passim in vols. 2 and 3 of Tax (n. 20 above).

28. Wilson (n. 7 above), p. 380.

29. Ibid., p. 386.

30. Ralph Wendell Burhoe, "Evolving Cybernetic Machinery and Human Values," *Zygon* 7 (1972): 188–209.

31. Manuscript record of the Symposia on Evolution and Man's Future, American Academy of Arts and Sciences, 1960.

32. Robert Boyd and Peter J. Richerson, "A Simple Dual Inheritance Model of the Conflict between Social and Biological Evolution," *Zygon* 11 (1976): 254-262.

33. John C. Kendrew, "Information and Conformation in Biology," in *Structural Chemistry and Molecular Biology,* ed. Alexander Rich and Norman Davidson (San Francisco: W. H. Freeman & Co., 1968), p. 193.

34. The quotation from Julian Huxley is from the University of Chicago [Darwin] centennial discussions, *Issues in Evolution,* Evolution after Darwin (n. 20 above), 3:213. The similar notions of H. J. Muller are found in his "Guidance of Human Evolution," in *The Evolution of Man: Mind, Culture, and Society,* Evolution after Darwin, 2:423–62, passim.

35. Emerson (n. 19 above).

36. Examples of scientists in whose writings the theory and supporting data for this picture of ritual behavior and the lower brain are, among biologists and ethologists, such persons as Dobzhansky, Wilson, Williams, C. H. Waddington, Niko Tinbergen, and Lorenz. Among anthropologists are such as Wallace, Ward H. Goodenough, Solomon H. Katz, and Clifford Geertz. Among psychologists are such as Eugene G. d'Aquili, Murray, and O. Hobart Mowrer. Among neurophysiologists are such as José M. R. Delgado, Hoagland, MacLean, Karl Pribram, and Sperry. These in many cases have published in past issues of *Zygon.* Others are publishing in this and future issues. The evidence for this conjoint evolution of genes and cultures and the role of religion has been piling up in the past couple of decades. The evidence for ritual communication originating more than a hundred million years ago is found in Lorenz's *On Aggression* (n. 9 above).

37. See, for instance, my "Natural Selection and God" (n. 17 above), or "The Concepts of God and Soul in a Scientific View of Human Purpose" (*Zygon* 8 [1973]: 412–42), or "Human Prospect" (n. 2 above).

38. N. 17 above.

39. My analysis of the relation of conscious and unconscious is akin to that of Erwin Schrödinger, P. W. Bridgman, and Sperry.

40. Bronowski (n. 2 above), p. 32. See also the confusion in Jacques Monod's *Chance and Necessity,* trans. Austryn Wainhouse (New York: Alfred A. Knopf, Inc., 1971), which Bronowski reduces.

41. See, for instance, Simon's *Sciences of the Artificial* (n. 1 above) or George Wald's "The Search for Common Ground" (*Zygon* 1 [1966]: 43–49).

7

Religion's Role in Human Evolution: The Missing Link between Ape-man's Selfish Genes and Civilized Altruism *

Drawing on an elaboration of recent scientific and scholarly evidence concerning the evolution of human nature, I seek to explain how it is that humans may manifest a kind of altruism not evident elsewhere in the biological world and to account for the unique role religion plays in the human segment of sociobiology. I am concerned also with the development of a more adequate scientific theory of religion, which perchance might revitalize religious belief, reverse a decline in altruism, and prevent a new "Dark Ages."

My general theory is that of a presently developing, general-systems evolutionary theory that seems to give new coherence to the description and explanation of the dynamic mechanisms that operate continually to extend the hierarchy of more or less stable states in cosmic evolution, states which include the persisting entities of biological and cultural evolution on earth and include even the microdynamics·of psychosocial development in individual persons.

This general-systems type of evolutionary theory is, as Eric J. Chaisson has pointed out, inherently interdisciplinary and provides an essentially value-orienting or religious understanding of man's place in the scheme of things.[1] A sector of that general-systems theory is sociobiology—a larger sector than

*This is a version of a paper presented at the Symposium on Sociobiology and Religion at the annual meeting of the American Psychological Association, Toronto, in 1978, a symposium in further response to Campbell's presidential address of 1975. It was first published in *Zygon* 14(2): 135–162, June 1979.

the psychological, black-box learning model and perhaps large enough to yield some understanding of religion and its capacity to engender altruistic behavior. I use the term "sociobiology" in the broad sense of Edward O. Wilson's definition: the "study of the biological basis of all social behavior."[2]

But we should note that biological patterns and behaviors are not limited to determination by genes alone, as many unsophisticated critics of sociobiology seem to fear. I think most good biologists, geneticists, and sociobiologists, when carefully read, will be found to be saying that organic structure and behavior are products of the interaction of the genetic information with a particular set of environing circumstances, including culture and other nonrandom and enduring factors, which properly have been called "paragenetic" information by such a veteran biological and evolutionary theorist as C. H. Waddington.[3]

The term "information" as used here in conjunction with genetic and paragenetic information signifies whatever it is that physically shapes, molds, or forms something. This is Webster's current, unabridged dictionary's first, but historically "obsolete," meaning and at the same time is very close to Webster's last and newest technical meaning of the term, used in such sciences as cybernetics that describe the negative feedback forces involved in the control or maintenance of suitable behavior in natural, organic, and artificial systems. (It is interesting to me that these first and last lexicological meanings of "information" are—through the implications of the operations of the brain as a neurophysiological machine for shaping organic response patterns by means of negative feedback mechanisms—inclusive of the more common lexical meanings of information.)

In short, both the genetic and the paragenetic sources of information (including the information in brains and cultures) are necessary and are inseparable in shaping the behaviors and patterns of living systems. Herbert A. Simon and others have gone so far as to point out that only a small (even though critical) part of the information that structures a living system can be or is found in the DNA of the genotype.[4] Hence S. L. Washburn was correct in his 1977 address to the American Psychological Association when he cautioned about some excessive claims by some so-called sociobiologists concerning the role of the DNA.[5]

But Washburn's caution in no way should diminish our excitement in the promise of sound sociobiology to help us better understand not only the social behavior of various levels of the animal kingdom but also the social behavior of mankind. Furthermore, this symposium on sociobiology and religion was stimulated as a response to Donald T. Campbell's bringing sociobiology to the attention of the American Psychological Association in his presidential address in 1975; and we are engaged here in examining his thesis that sociobiology helps us understand the positive and natural role religion has played in generating altruistic behavior in admittedly selfish humans.[6]

Campbell has been recognized as a most significant pioneer in refining and enlarging various elements of the intellectual toolbox of the psychosocial sciences. But in his presidential address to the association he shocked many of his colleagues in both the physicalist-determinist camp and the humanistic-therapeutic camp. In his introduction he suggested that—of all things—traditional religions were, "on purely scientific grounds, . . . better tested [recipes for living] than the best of psychology's and psychiatry's [scientifically unverified] speculations." At the same time he pointed out that genetics and "hard-line neo-Darwinian" evolutionary theory—of all things—support his picture of the role of religion as superior to that of psychotherapy for either understanding or generating human altruism.

In his conclusion Campbell summarized:

Urban humanity is a product of both biological and social evolution. Evolutionary genetics shows that, when there is genetic competition among the cooperators (as [is the case] for humans but not for social insects), great limitations are placed upon the degree of socially useful, individually self-sacrificial altruism that [genetic] evolution can produce. Human social complexity is a product of social [but not only genetic] evolution [where the culturally transmitted information is accumulated under a program of "blind variation and systematic selective retention" analogous to that of the genes] and has had to counter with inhibitory moral norms the biological selfishness which genetic competition has selected continually.[7]

In general I think Campbell's broad scientific picture of human nature is correct. I recognize him as a creative pioneer in providing here some sound bridges uniting the psychosocial, biological, and humanistic islands of our contemporary culture's understandings of human nature. His contribution to our understanding of the independent but analogous evolution of culture alongside genetic information is outstanding and is an essential complement to genetics in a maturing discipline of sociobiology. His pioneering of a scientifically based account of religion's role in human evolution is so far ahead of the understanding of many colleagues in the psychosocial sciences that it took great courage for him to dare to speak of it in his presidential address to the psychological community. I opined, as I observed the responses at the meeting and reflected on what I have heard in discussions and seen in the literature, that for many of the psychological community his introduction of genetics was beyond the pale of both their understanding and their views of relevance. But even more, his introduction of the concept of the natural but nongenetic selection of culture and of nature thus endowing religion with an essential function in life was simply out of their capacity to conceive. I know how he agonized in advance of his presentation about how much he might dare say about these results of his research.

I shall give a brief overview of some extensions of his theory to provide the kinds of developments and corrections which I think he would be among the first to encourage—in fact he already has formally done so in various ways, including his suggestion that I participate in this symposium. My efforts, like Campbell's and Wilson's, toward a scientific understanding of the sources of human altruism have been in progress over a number of years. I believe I have a piece in the picture puzzle that is a necessary addition not only to Campbell's but also to Wilson's in order to make scientific sense. I call this missing piece, in a play upon words used in an earlier problem of evolutionary theory, the "missing link" between ape-man's selfish genes and civilized altruism. For background we must turn to Wilson's picture.

The Paradox of Human Altruism for Sociobiology

In his classic *Sociobiology: The New Synthesis,* published in 1975, Wilson notes that:

to visualize the main features of social behavior in all organisms at once, from colonial jellyfish to man, is to encounter a paradox. We should first note that social systems have originated repeatedly in one major group of organisms after another, achieving widely different degrees of specialization and complexity. Four groups occupy pinnacles high above the others: the colonial invertebrates, the social insects, the non-human mammals, and man. . . . Although the sequence just given proceeds from unquestionably more primitive and older forms of life to more advanced and recent ones, the key properties of social existence, including cohesiveness, altruism, and cooperativeness, decline. It seems as though social evolution has slowed as the body plan of the individual organism became more elaborate.[8]

Wilson then points out that the basic mechanism of genetic selection plays a major role in this since the possibility of genetic programming of social cooperation is maximum and unlimited for organisms with genetic identity and, because of the mechanisms involved in natural selection, falls off as the individuals in a society become less close kin. As the degree of kinship or genetic identity among the individuals in a society decreases, so does the degree of altruistic cooperation, as one surveys the characteristics that have emerged over the last billion years to constitute these four successive pinnacles of social evolution—from complete identity of genotypes and high social cooperation among the individual organisms that constitute a jellyfish, down to a two-thirds relationship and a lesser cooperation in the societies of ants and other social hymenoptera, down to one-half or less relationship in many mammalian societies, which necessarily are much smaller in size and at best have much lower levels of altruistic behavior.

But the great paradox comes when we note that out of the mammalian group called apes there have emerged human societies, which may have large populations of individuals with little or no genetic kinship relation but which manifest such high degrees of cooperation and altruism as to reverse the downward trend of social evolution Wilson noted in the previous sequence from lower to higher forms. This human phenomenon so completely bypasses the genetic requirements and facts concerning altruism that Wilson has called it the "culminating mystery of all biology."[9]

I suggest this mystery may be explained in terms of well-understood biological theory if we can show, as I think we can, that human sociocultural organisms constitute in effect a new, transgenetic living species capable of symbiosis (of the "social mutualism" type) with populations of ape-men.[10]

Evolutionary Background of Religion as the Missing Link

Here I must only summarize some basic elements of my conclusions in this matter. I stand with the hard core of those who find that genes by their nature cannot program favors for competing genes since any risk to themselves would bring them to the end of their line—natural selection's way of operating.[11] Therefore I hold that genes cannot be selected to program an organism to provide gifts that benefit another organism except when the benefits given do not reduce the inclusive fitness of the donor's genetic line. But under some circumstances such a donor's inclusive fitness is enhanced rather than reduced, as when the gift is (1) for very close kin, to serve whom is also to serve one's own genetic line; (2) for nonkin spouses, to serve whom is also to serve one's own genetic line; and (3) for nonrelated organisms which for some reason happen to be programmed to provide some degree of reciprocally beneficial services for the donor's genetic line. For all such self-giving of a phenotype we have copious evidence that genes are selected; but for understanding human society the third case, "reciprocal altruism," is of primary interest.[12]

Reciprocal altruism among nonrelated organisms is very common as a genetically programmed, reciprocally beneficial behavior between many kinds of species, whereby the organisms of one species provide benefits for those of the other species in what is called symbiotic cooperation. Since there can be no allelic competition with the genes of other species, symbiotic altruism bypasses natural selection's bar to programming genetic production of altruism among conspecific but nonkin organisms. One species coadapts at the genetic level to interact with the other, just as it adapts to any other factor in its environment.[13] In this way the gene pools of two or more species may become coadapted to produce cooperation that is so close that a casual observer may not be able to distinguish that what appears to be a single organism of cooperating parts is in reality an ecosystem of two or more symbiotic but very distinct species genetically coadapted to cooperate in a socially symbiotic system—such as flagellates endosymbiotic in termites or primitive prokaryotic organelle species endosymbiotic in human cells.[14]

Within a species, however—since any consequences of what an altruistic gene does to favor a competing gene's relative frequency in a population will diminish its own frequency and tend to its own elimination—it seems logically impossible for any gene to be selected to generate altruistic self-sacrifice in order to benefit other genes. As I have pointed out, some genetic theorists such as George C. Williams therefore have asserted that natural selection cannot favor the selection of genes that would produce altruism toward other members of the population or group except toward those who carry the same genes.

The same genes may be continued through one's offspring and the offspring of close relatives. Hence phenotypic altruism—the risk or sacrifice of the body in order to insure the continuity of one's genes through offspring—is a behavior that nature does select. As a matter of fact, since DNA eventually deteriorates and would bring an individual organism eventually to death, the life cycle—which includes reproduction of multiple sets of genes to continue in a new generation of organisms and includes the death of the old body—serves as a filtering process to maintain or enhance the value of the gene pool. Only the viable genes pass through this filter, and they may be multiplied or increased in frequency by the phenomena of the transient life cycle of an organism. Thus organisms by nature are selected to be sacrificial of themselves for the greater treasure for life that inheres in the continuity and enhancement of the wisdom of the genes. Hence altruism toward or cooperation with spouses, kin, and any agency that would enhance the "inclusive fitness" (the continuity of genes like one's own, as in offspring) can be understood readily.

While Williams and others have argued from this picture that we cannot expect anything but selfishness from genes and that the mechanism of selection among competing alleles is not likely to produce altruism except altruism that enhances the donor's inclusive fitness, Wilson and others have been more concerned to see if altruism to nonkin may be explained by some mechanisms of selecting genes through the selection of a group, population, or deme for its virtues instead of through selection of an individual organism for its virtues. Wilson summarizes the efforts toward such an explanation in chapter 5, entitled "Group Selection and Altruism," of his *Sociobiology*. There are indeed some theoretical models. But, as Wilson reports, "the evidence for interdemic selection is fragmentary and somewhat peculiar in nature"; "in spite of the frequently permissible conditions that exist in nature, actual cases of interdemic selection have only rarely been reported in the literature." He also notes in reporting on the altruism involved in warning calls that there seem to be more theoretical difficulties with explanation by interdemic selection than by kin selection or individual selection. In reporting on other evidences of altruism he points out that it is often equally or better explained by kin and individual selection. Nevertheless, he concludes his chapter by leaving the door open on whether group selection can explain altruism.

My studies of religion, human nature, and biological theory all cohere in leading me to agree with the view of Williams and others that the genes must be inherently selfish. For me the altruism of phenotypes or organisms for the genes is in fact an altruism for the sacred and has been selected to operate that way analogously to the selection of human self-sacrificial altruism for the sacred or religious core of culture. Moreover, I find that Wilson's own eloquent demonstration of the decline of altruism with the decline in the index of genetic relatedness itself argues strongly against any genetic programs for altruism except when it enhances the donor's inclusive fitness.

Richard Dawkins in his *The Selfish Gene* has provided an excellent and generally readable account for this case. He also has introduced a plausible scientific account of cultural evolution under the "natural selection" of cultural information, akin to the views advanced by Campbell and me. He calls the information units in culture "memes" in analogy with genes. In the 1950s Henry Alexander Murray similarly had suggested we call them "idenes." In reading Dawkins I felt that he may have introduced his last-chapter excursion into cultural evolution in an effort to explain human altruism, which just could not be explained by natural selection of genes. But Dawkins rightly concludes that memes, by selection from among competing individuals, are bound to be just as selfish as genes. Unfortunately, after concluding this, he quickly finishes his book with an admittedly lame hope for any explanation of human altruism.[15]

But there is a solution to our problem of accounting for human as well as insect altruism by natural selection. I already have noted how natural selection brings about altruism between species without running into the problem of competing alleles in any natural-selection mechanism of either genes or memes—the problem that forced Dawkins and many others to declare quite honestly that not only are genes utterly selfish but so are the memes (or idenes) of the cultural information that rides piggyback on, and modifies the expression of, the genotype. But what if we should discover upon careful examination that culturetypes and their expression in sociocultural organisms are an independent "species" of living substance symbiotic with populations of *Homo*—selected independently because the units of selection, while dependent upon a human population, are not dependent upon any particular human population? What if, to speak in a dynamic analogy, the sociocultural organism and its culturetype were as independent of what anthropoid population flows through it as a whirlpool of a particular configuration that is shaped by its stream bed is independent of which population of water molecules flow through it? Does this happen in life?

The differences among religions, languages, particular technologies, and other sociocultural interaction configurations or customs may be very little shaped by the particular genetics of the populations that are thus encultured so long as the normal distribution of genes in these populations is not too divergent from the normal distribution of genes in the larger gene pool from which the particular culture draws its population. A language can be learned and effectively used by almost any genetic population of humans. But no complex language can be confined to a population as small as an extended family or can be as short-lived as a generation. The lifetime and space dimensions of sociocultural structures and organisms (and of the memory banks or stream beds that are essential for characterizing them) are, I suggest, of quite different dimensions from those of the individual ape-men. The ape-men are the "water

drops" that contribute the "substance" of a sociocultural configuration that is shaped by a nongenetic memory bank.

If cultural patterns are of such different dimensions that they
are not selected by the same selectors for whose benefits
individual organisms compete, they can evolve independently.
What if there indeed has emerged in human evolution a new
living entity that organizes not just the individuals in a family of
genetic kin but any number of individuals provided they represent a fair sample of the population of human genotypes?
What if this sociocultural organizing entity is able to integrate
populations of thousands or millions into serving it, in return
for its enhancing the probability of the genetic lines of a
significant sample of a population over what would be the case
in any competing ecological niche? What if such sociocultural
organizers or organisms do compete in fact for limited
resources and some are better?

The great puzzle of explaining human reciprocal altruism
spread through a large population of nonkin conspecifics disappears should it be the case that there is an independent
"species" to which ape-men are coadapted to serve. Their
behavior could be explained as genetically produced reciprocity with a creature of different "species" and not necessarily
providing genetic benefits for conspecifics that contemporary
genetic theory denies apart from inclusive fitness. We are quite
familiar with the adaptation of a species to any source of
benefits, including various other species. And we have numerous cases of the coadaptation of two or more species into a
common ecosystem that may give the appearance of a single
organism, so closely knit are their functions and so invisible
have they been to our previous capacities for perceiving or
conceiving. Moreover, we can explain such cooperation in
terms of natural selection of genes.

But in humans we probably have the first such symbiotic
system, constituting an apparently unitary living creature, in
which one of the symbionts is not programmed by DNA but by
cultural information, independently transmitted and selected.
What is new in the ecosystem that constitutes a human society
is not that one of the symbionts utilizes for its own phenotype
the phenotypic substance or patterns generated by the programs of the DNA of the other symbiont, for that relation is

common and is the relation between our prokaryotic and eukaryotic cells. What is new is that the separate and "species-specific" package of information generating the symbiont we call the sociocultural organism is not a genotype but a culturetype. If individual ape-men are bonded by the coadaptation of their genes in a symbiotic service to a sociocultural organism that is also an evolving system of living substance independent of any particular human genotypes and yet that binds its anthropoid population to serve it in exchange for reciprocal benefits provided by the species-specific behaviors selected in the coadaptation, then our paradox disappears. The paradox here, as in the sciences generally, is resolved by revising our model or presuppositions until we have found a better fit between our conceptual system and the actual events it models.

There are hundreds of fascinating details to be more fully worked out in my model for resolving this problem, such as the origin, nature, and stability of culturetypes. But there is also much evidence that seems to confirm the picture. Here I can consider only some primary features.

In short, my hypothesis is that sociocultural systems are "organisms" of a new living kingdom, quite different from either the animal or plant kingdoms of ordinary biology, and are beneficent "parasites," so to say, which are completely dependent upon the special animal species *Homo sapiens,* as a *Homo* cell is dependent upon prokaryotes for the necessary substance of its life. The sociocultural organisms have been almost as hidden from our scientific view as the alien but essential prokaryotic creatures that are such necessary agencies in each of our eukaryotic cells. The sociocultural organisms are equally real and essential to our being human.

The sociocultural organisms are a species with which ape-men are endosymbiotic. But one can say not only that as individuals we live within a sociocultural organism but also that the sociocultural organism lives within us. Not only are we individual units within an organized society, but organized society is represented and incarnated within our brains. Hence we can say that according to one kind of analysis the sociocultural organisms are endosymbiotic in the brain of man—much of a total society's "culturetype" may lie in an individual brain.

In fact, in primitive societies the primary locus of the culturetype is the reiterated incarnations in brain after brain of the
patterns of the language, customs, and socially transmitted
values that characterize the sociocultural organism. Apart from
the sociocultural organism, whether viewed as the product of
the enculturated patterns inside an individual brain or viewed
as the coordinated and mutually supportive patterns of
behavior in a city or nation that result from such incarnations,
the human individual loses his humanity and becomes a rather
helpless hominid, inviable in a nonenculturating habitat.

It may help if it is understood that I am describing human
nature in a physicalistic, scientific conceptual system. Within
this conceptual system the research findings of the past few
decades have been making it possible to describe man with the
greatest degree of coherence and clarity thus far. This is
especially true for understanding how our conscious and
aesthetic commonsense views of ourselves are related to our
physical bodies, to the society of other persons, and to the
whole complex environment within which we live and move
and have our being. As F. S. C. Northrop pointed out some
thirty years ago, the physical conceptual system is the crowning
epistemological tool achieved in the West for providing coherent and "objective" views or "truth" in theology as well as in
the sciences in general. It is by using this model that I am
putting together in this paper such varied facets of human
nature ranging over the spectrum of disciplines ("ways of
talking") from subjective, spiritual, cultural, religious, esthetic
(feeling, emotions, values), social, economic, biological, chemical, to physical—with the modifiers "objective" and "true"
being applicable all the way along, according to one's system of
definitions. I cannot elaborate this recent scientific development of the old philosophical "epistemology" and "ontology"
here but simply assert that if one tries to read what I am saying
about language, culture, brains, societies, morals, religion, and
theology in this paper in the physicalistic languages of physical
and chemical systems into which I assert they all can be
translated neatly, then one perhaps will come to enjoy the
unified picture I see, a picture that provides for a rational
integration of many of the confusions of our present historical
epoch. Some, according to their background in the various

disciplinary jargons or ways of talking, will have to accept on faith that all my translations into a physicalistic language are valid and that the physicalistic model operates to explain and make coherent all the otherwise disjunctive bits and pieces.[16] With this digression to help understand more clearly what I am trying to do, let us return to some of the concrete aspects of our discussion of religion's role in human evolution and continue with our summary of our hypothesis concerning the emergence and nature of human culture in the evolutionary scene, a scene in which culture is interlocked with biology, chemistry, and the physics of the cosmos.

In my model of cultural evolution the heritage of information comes packaged as a culturetype, made up of units as in Dawkins's memes or Murray's idenes. The culturetype is of course an analogue of the genotype only in a general sense, the detailed mechanisms being quite different. The corresponding dynamics are still obscure. A culturetype provides the information which, in interaction with the human gene pool and other elements of its ecological niche, produces the ecosystemic phenotype that we know as a human society. The information package that is the culturetype is symbiotic to the point of parasitic dependence upon the brains of a population of *Homo*. It is transmitted to and from a storage "gland," one might say, which is at the other end of the spinal column from that of the gonad, namely, the neopallium of the brain. This culturetypic information is what shapes the specific characteristics of a sociocultural organism—its particular language, technologies, rituals, mores, myths, institutions, etc.[17]

A culturetype, as an information packet which is "extra-specific" to the gene pool of *Homo,* operates on a population of ape-men in a way analogous to a virus that infects only the outer cortex of the brain, using the brain as a resource for its own propagation. This theory provides a proper basis for the natural selection of memes and hence of culturetypes, independently from (although always constrained to be symbiotically coadapted with) the genes and genotypes of *Homo*.

While the theory of the natural selection of cultures is now in as confused or vague a state as that of the natural selection of genes was a half-century ago, I believe that recent work has provided grounds for a new understanding of human nature that has as much potential as did the genetic theories earlier for understanding animal nature. In particular I believe that my symbiosis model provides a conceptual framework adequate for explaining Wilson's "culminating mystery of all biology" — human altruism — and for revitalizing religion.

My model of the relation between culturetypes and gene pools as symbiotic and of the culturally transmitted information as undergoing a kind of natural selection is one somewhat akin to that proposed by Campbell. However, my model differs from Campbell's in that I do not hypothesize that cultural information can fight or overcome genetic information to provide altruism, which is the way I read his presidential address. I do not see how any constraint that conflicts with the basic requirements to which the genotype has adapted can be viable. Moreover, I stand with Dawkins in seeing that cultural information units are as inherently "selfish" as genetic information units and for analogous reasons which derive from any mechanism of natural selection from among competing units.

Campbell too sees cultural selection as the product of random variations and selective retention in an operation that is logically or mathematically analogous to the selection of genetic DNA packages, and he first called my attention in the late 1960s to the overpowering logic and evidence of Williams in *Adaptation and Natural Selection* to the effect that one cannot expect selection of competing alleles to produce behavior that favors one's competitor.[18] But I do not find that Campbell presents a convincing case on how cultural practices can defy the genetic requirements. My systems theoretical approach forces me into the traditional biological view of the opportunism in evolutionary processes which are forced to build stage n on stage $n-1$ and so on down the hierarchy. If genes are built of molecules, genes use the molecular natures and behaviors in special ways to accomplish the adapted ends of genes and organisms. If cultures are built of genetically programmed animal populations, I suspect cultures use those populations according to the given animal natures in the populations to accomplish adaptations to cultural ends.

I already have referred to Dawkins's failure to explain human altruism.[19] But regardless of the incompleteness of Campbell's or Dawkins's or other efforts to resolve this biologically anomalous problem of altruism, it seems to me quite clearly solvable on very traditional biological information. Reciprocal altruism between individuals in a population of humans and a sociocultural organism clearly can come from natural selection, if there is indeed a symbiosis between two separate "species." This kind of reciprocal altruism is one that various investigators have found established between the coadapted gene pools of many combinations of separate but symbiotic species, such as the prokaryotic organelles which are endosymbiotic in the eukaryotic cells of humans or the flagellate protozoan species that are endosymbiotic in the digestive tracts of termites. The resultant phenotypes are so tightly interdependent that they have become an ecosystemic organism, or what Alfred E. Emerson called a "supraorganism."[20]

Like the flagellate in the termite, an individual ape-man who is endosymbiotic within a cultural organism does not so much serve his fellow humans individually (except close kin and mates, which he serves under genetic programming naturally selected under competition of alternate alleles) as he serves the sociocultural organism. He serves the sociocultural organism because of the reciprocal altruism built into both the cultural organism "species" and the ape-man species by the coadaptation of their noncompeting information packages.[21]

If our analysis that each human individual is not a single organism but an element of a symbiotic ecosystem or supraorganism is confirmed, then each of us can be seen as motivated (programmed) simultaneously by the two separate, semiindependent but coadapted information systems that have emerged as the significant determinants in our analysis of human behavior: genotype and culturetype. To the extent that culturetypes do program significant differences of the mean goal orientation (values) and behavior patterns of the phenotypes in two population groups from what is contributed by the differences in the gene pools of the two populations, the new phenomenon of unprecedented and mystifying phenotypic altruism pointed out by Wilson can be explained by the culturetypes of the ape-man. Since the significant features of an ape-man's culturetype may be essentially identical with the culturetype of the other ape-men whose ecological niche is the same cultural organism, his "index of relatedness"—in terms of his cultural, not genetic, heritage—may approach the unity of an "identical twin."

In other words, if my model of selection in the evolution of a culture (a model in part shared by Campbell and Dawkins) is valid, if cultural information is selected independently of genetic information (provided only that its selection yields coadaptation toward symbiosis), if interaction goals between individuals sometimes are dominated by the culturetypic aspects of our motivating system (this is highly plausible when the genetic aspects are not in conflict), and if some mathematical analogues of the genotypic relatedness index also apply to the fostering of phenotypic altruism in the expression of culturetypes, then, since the cultural relatedness of most members of the same culture may be more than the three-quarter relationship found in the genotypes of hymenopteran societies (and perhaps in some cases as much as the unity relatedness index of the colonial microorganism societies), we may have an explanation on the basis of an analogue of genetic natural selection for the very mystifying human behavior of risking one's life even more readily for one's spiritual or cultural "brother" than for one's genetic brother. Insofar as the cultural brother is an identical twin in the "value core" of his culturetype, and to the degree that under the circumstances the culturetype is operative in determining one's behavior, to that extent one can expect motivation for such extremes of altruism as have not been seen, Wilson points out, since the first phylogenetic peak of altruism.[22]

To be sure, the potential relationship of unity in the culturetype segment of the human phenotype's programming is diluted by the degree in which the genotype determines the behavior in a particular circumstance. It also is diluted by the degree in which the culturetype lacks the features specified above. Moreover, I do not see how the symbiotic coadaptation of culturetype and genotype statistically can repay the genes for risks to the phenotype too much above the level of the norms obtaining in mammalian groups generally. Nevertheless, human nature has manifested various levels of these altruistic behaviors and has included the saints as well as the most selfish sinners. The point is that this model allows for an explanation of both, as a function of the coadaptedness of genotypes with culturetypes in particular populations and circumstances. It provides a sociobiological picture that may be able to explain many of the intriguing features of human nature and behavior that hitherto have been indeed a mystery to the sciences of man. It also may prove useful for aiding humanity in any intentional efforts that it may make to adapt to higher patterns of life.

But I must leave unsaid a lot of what needs saying about the two natures or information packages that program man and how they are interrelated at neurophysiological levels. For purposes of this paper I must move quickly to a brief review of the significance of religion in this mechanism for generating the strange phenomenon of human altruism.

Once More: Religion Seen Scientifically

Before discussing religion's role in human evolution to resolve the culminating mystery of all biology, I must digress to provide a brief picture of religion seen scientifically. Many of my colleagues in the scientific and secular world understand the term "religion" to refer only to obsolete myth. It is characteristic that writers like Campbell, Dawkins, Wilson, and others are quite ready seriously to involve religion to explain how in ancient history human societies larger than kinfolk tribes were established and maintained. But it would seem that the "current culture" picture of religion as henceforth irrelevant must be replaced by a more scientific one if they are to resolve the paradox of human altruism.

Religion, I suggest, is the key and hitherto missing link in the scientific explanation of how ape-men are transformed to civilized altruism. Religion—as I am using the term—is the system of rituals, myths, rational theologies, etc., that constitute and convey our basic heritage of culturally communicated values. Values are patterns of information that shape the goals of behavior, that structure the cybernetic mechanisms in our bodies and nervous systems that determine what we love or hate, want or fear, go for or flee from, etc. Hence values shape our overall behavior patterns and the way we spend our lives. Technically values are the norms of our cybernetic mechanisms. Every creature has basic values, and these are shaped or determined ultimately by the information in its genotype, which shapes the cybernetic mechanisms for admitting benefits and rejecting harmful substances through cell walls and also shapes the neurochemical structures of brains that coordinate the value hierarchies of complex organisms.

But in humans, if my earlier analysis is right, there are two separate natures—one shaped by the genotype and the other shaped by the culturetype—which are packages of structuring information coadapted by natural selection as they evolved during the past million years, although the culturetypes have made some major step jumps in their evolutionary rate during the past few centuries, few thousand years, and few ten-thousand-year periods. During these periods religions have emerged as the agencies or cybernetic mechanisms for coordinating the coadaptation between the basic values of genotypes and culturetypes. There are genetic components for religion as well as for language, but both are primarily dependent upon sociocultural transmission so far as particular sociocultural structuring and dynamics are concerned.[23] As such, religious information is transmitted from brain to brain where it operates to modify the expression of the information supplied by the varied genotypes in the population so as to give viable attitudes, feelings, and goals. In other words, viable attitudes, feelings, and goals are the cybernetic norms of "ultimate concern" in a population, to use the theologian Paul Tillich's term for characterizing religion.

While humans—and all other symbiotic systems that behave as a single organism or supraorganism—have two or more semiindependent core packages of information that program their behavior, their selection as a viable ecosystemic unit—it must be recalled—requires that natural selection sufficiently coadapt the separate information packages so that their interaction in a particular habitat will produce in fact a viable ecosystemic or symbiotic unit. Hence, according to my hypothesis, religions have been selected—both through the transformations of genetic information in the generations of ape-men and the cultural information in the generations of sociocultural organisms—to integrate the values of both coadapted systems. (I must warn quickly anyone who has not studied my previous work in this area that the term "generations" of sociocultural organism should not imply the same kind of mechanisms of variation and selection as that involved in genotypes, and most of us working in the field do not conceive of such simplistic analogues any more that good evolutionary biologists conceive of the analogous genotypes of flying bugs, birds, and bats as homologous). I should indicate also that I have shown in other papers some of the evidence that this particular formulation of the nature of religion in terms of scientific categories does conform to a remarkable degree with religion known through prescientific historical, philosophical, and commonsense languages.

Religions at the sociocultural level are the product jointly of the culturetype and of the society's gene pool. Religions at the level of personal behavior and experience are similarly the product of the culturetype and genetically only of the particular genotype of the individual person. Religions are the agency of coadaptation or synthesis of the individual's unique, genotypically programmed system of values and his values as structured by his symbiont sociocultural organism, so that he becomes indeed a suitably coadapted product of the interaction of two separate species—ape-man and sociocultural organism. Our psychotherapeutic and religious terms suggesting the desirability of integration and wholeness are testimony to this nature and the need for integrating the two systems.[24]

If either the genotype or the culturetype is not well coadapted, the one with the other, then the individual person experiences the inner conflict between his "bodily" and his "spiritual" natures, to express it in Saint Paul's language. But when they are all well coadapted the torturing conflict disappears, as in Saint Paul's interpretation of Christian salvation, and is replaced by a natural joy in giving one's self in gracious love to the service of one's fellow humans, confident in the hope that one's ultimate or long-term rewards, guaranteed by the superhuman Lord of History, will be greater than the temporary sacrifices that one now renders for such an outcome. A human being who in his culturally informed brain can regain a culturally unspoiled, pristine, genotypically programmed trust of the essentially good relationship between himself and the ultimate source of his being can keep his sophisticated culture and yet reenter the paradise of primitive animal innocence and trust—and live confidently in this world, being possessed of a sound hope and as free from overweening anxiety or fear of inevitable, natural death and multiple other hazards as the birds of the air and the lilies of the field. Good religions have functioned to release ape-men's brains from the overload of anxieties about the primitive culture's natural world. The potential for emotional overload increased with the evolutionary rapid increase of the brain's outer layers. These layers mediated associative and predictive powers and communication of information by language. The emotional charge of linguistic information input was not susceptible to harmonious adaptation to each individual's genetic information since linguistic communication was the statistical product of the brains in a genetically diverse interacting population. It thus became necessary for any culturetype that had evolved linguistic communication also to evolve a religion that could adapt successfully, to the particular needs of the average individual in its population, the impact (in terms of meaning, values, or emotion) of the enlarged, unfiltered, and sometimes maladaptive information load.

It should be noted that religions are cybernetic mechanisms and not simply the opiates, indeed, as Karl Marx suggested. That is, religions present the other side inherent in any control mechanisms: the stimulus to action as well as the prevention of overloads that terrorize and immobilize. As Campbell and others correctly note, religions have been the source of moral and other stimulus in our sociocultural control mechanism. They have been indeed a vital mechanism for the possibility of altruism to a total community beyond the nuclear family.

However, in the past few centuries the new revelations by the sciences have destroyed for many the effectiveness of the symbolic expressions of earlier religious belief systems that engendered proper confidence about the nature of the self in the context of that upon which it is dependent for life and that engendered a proper sense of duty and hope in the same context. There has been lost a needed conviction or faith in a system of transhuman powers that define our meaning and destiny and sanction our loyalties and morals in our sociocultural organism. Lost also is the equally necessary belief concerning the salvation of our souls in the end, if we behave properly.

As a result there is a sickness spreading simultaneously

through our sociocultural organism and in the "hearts" (brains' limbic systems?) of the populations of poorly humanized ape-men. There is a widespread literature on this anomie and anxiety that seems to be increasing as sociocultural prophets from Fyodor Dostoevski to Aleksandr Solzhenitsyn seek to point out the dangerousness of our situation. There is a considerable and growing consensus on the dire symptoms, some consensus on the diagnosis of humanity's illness—but little on the cure.

It is my conviction that the cure is at hand and a new epoch in human history will begin when we can reformulate our heritage of sociocultural values and truths so as to interpret them in the light or context of present science. I find strong evidence that the general structure of this culturetypic heritage, found in the religions of the world, has been long selected by the same reality or nature that has selected our gene pools. In this selection process various culturetypes have been coadapted with the wisdom of the gene pool in very subtle and not yet very fully understood ways so as to guide the successive stages of genetic expression into complex patternings of non-kin, conspecific individuals whose behavior cooperates in such ways as to produce the emergence and evolution of the unprecedented phenomenon of sociocultural organisms at an accelerating pace up into the contemporary age of science. But the emergence of modern science, like the emergence of writing and of philosophy, poses not only miraculous opportunities but grave threats to the basic values that sustain man's symbiotic synthesis. Therefore I see as today's most important task for mankind the effort to unite religious and scientific beliefs into a union that can provide again a successful symbiosis of genotypes and culturetypes—but now within the new sociocultural ecological niche produced by modern science and technology where traditional formulations of religious belief have become less adequate as maps of reality and grounds for action. Such a union of religious and scientific beliefs has become possible as recent scientific and scholarly studies of religion have provided new insights into the wisdom that has been selected by the processes that have created human life and culture, as Campbell has helped make clear. This allows new translations or interpretations of religious wisdom in the light of scientific concepts and the revitalization of that wisdom for an age of science.[25]

At this point I turn from a brief outline of religion seen in the light of the sciences to show how such an understanding of religion can move us—farther than Campbell, Dawkins, or Wilson has yet supposed—to resolve sociobiology's paradox of human altruism.

How Do Religions Resolve Sociobiology's Paradox?

How have religions specifically operated to generate the necessary altruism for human societies—the first large and complex societies of conspecific organisms that are not close kin to appear in evolution of life on earth? Here I shall give only a brief characterization of the religious function in generating the minimal threshold of faith—and hence of practice—that altruistic acts to the cultural organism would be reciprocated. A nervous system not programmed with a confidence in such reciprocation would not be compatible or coadapted with the underlying motivations programmed by its genotype and hence would not succeed. Such a confidence or faith is prerequisite to the practice of reciprocal altruism.

Reciprocal altruism among conspecifics might be genetically sustained, Wilson points out using data from S. A. Boorman and P. R. Levitt, if a certain critical frequency of an "altruist gene" were to be reached. But he notes that we are still left with the problem of how such critical frequencies can be reached.[26] As I have pointed out, this problem does not exist in cooperating behavior between one species and another. Therefore genetic selection of reciprocal altruism is natural for a population of ape-men coadapting to an extraspecific, benign, culturetypic "virus." The symbiosis of ape-men with a sociocultural organism requires a harmoniously binding connection, in each brain of the ape-man population, between the implicit requirements and promises of the sociocultural organism (which are encoded in each ape-man's neocortex) and the implicit requirements and promises of the genetically programmed norms in the lower brain structures of each ape-man, structures that provide the basic fears, desires, and other motivations. Each sociocultural organism is phenotypically "parasitic" upon a population of *Homo,* where its culturetype is encoded in the brain's outer layers, which by coadaptation have been programmed readily to incorporate culturetypic patterns transmitted from brain to brain in the sociocultural community, including the patterns of the language and other symbol systems.[27]

The most primitive stages of religion, according to this analysis, begin with and ever must depend upon genetically programmed, animal-ritual communication—for example, bowing the head as a sign of submission that is common in mammalian populations. The initially genetically programmed, animal-ritual communications system among individual ape-men already is included in the neurological connections between the cybernetic norms of their primitive social life and the norms of the motivational mechanisms in the lower or reptilian levels of our brains. It was through this connection that primitive cultural organisms could enculturate the particular refinements that paragenetically guide the "expression" of the genetically programmed symbols of good and evil. There are several hierarchical stages of this neuronal mechanism for transforming response to signals of good or evil.[28]

These stages are illumined by recent psychological studies of stages of human ontogeny, such as those by Jean Piaget and Lawrence Kohlberg. It would seem probable that the phylogenetic stages of sociocultural organisms were akin to those still necessary in the ontogeny of our essentially anthropoid organisms (chimpanzee and gorilla genes differ from *Homo* by less that 1 percent) into civilized humans.[29] This is why there is so much ritual communication in even the higher religions; motivation always requires ultimate stimulation all the way down to the basic, genetically programmed motivational mechanisms. I see no escape from ultimate satisfaction of the basic genetic requirements, and I can see no culturetype succeeding that does not cooperate to fulfill such genetic requirements. But when the paragenetic patterns of a viable culturetype are well coadapted with these the resultant norms or values of both systems are integrated. And when these norms are adapted to the larger environing ecosystem so that this subecosystem is viable in the larger one they are what the philosophers have called "intrinsic values." In evolutionary

theory of course such basic values never can be absolute for all
time but must be evolving continually to adapt to new conditions that occur with the passage of time.[30]

Above the stages of basic ritual communication, as our
ancestors began to have brains that allowed symbolic communication involving neurological codes in which symbolic
models of self and world were patterned inside the head, they
began to talk and to conceptualize. They used language to
communicate explanations of hitherto unperceived relations of
cause and effect among the events of their experiences. There
began to evolve the stories to explain the puzzling mysteries of
life, mysteries because the newly evolved but quite finite
logical computer in the brain (coadapted with programs fed to
it from an emerging culturetype) gradually opened the win-
dows of perception or conception upon a scene of infinite
complexity. In this complexity there naturally arose misunder-
standings that seemed to threaten the core values of the living
system as "comprehended" by the more limited perspective of
the genotype. The rising anxieties connected with expanding
awareness of death and other threats always had to be dealt
with by each brain, usually with the help of a culturetypic
heritage that already had made a more or less satisfactory
adaptation to the problem.

The culturetypes became adapted through the selective process by evolving new, paragenetic information input to give
more adequate models of the self and its environment and
hence more adequate models of what to seek or avoid—good
and evil. This information, by its nature, was not and could not
be encoded as such in the gene pool. Yet culturetypes always
had to defer to the basic demands of the gene pools, with which
they were symbiotic, or else be selected out. The culturetypi-
cally transformed prescriptions (whether at conscious or the
more usual unconscious levels is immaterial) of what to do that
did not immediately satisfy the genetic norms of the lower
brain structures had to be "explained" as somehow ultimately
fulfilling the implicit goals of the genotype. A present post-
ponement of an instinctively warranted good could be negoti-
ated successfully only if there was a credible promise of a later
payment with a still larger good.

One has to suppose the gradual evolution of the culturetypes of various sociocultural organisms to accumulate a stock of descriptions, prescriptions, and warrants optimally coadapted with the available genetic and environmental requirements for viability. A statistically successful delivery of the payment of the postponed reciprocal rewards to the faithful servants of the sociocultural organism was experienced in fact (with a consequently enhanced inclusive fitness for the surviving gene pool of that population); otherwise individual ape-men deserted that particular culture or their gene pool thereby was diminished in fitness. The religious stories or myths had to be "true" in basic consequences for life and became so by the natural selection of culturetypes along with genes. Thus religious wisdom became sacred, and the gods were real.

The stories or myths had to explain to each member of the population, in forms meaningful to its stock of symbolic structures, why and how certain culturally evolved requirements should be acted upon, even though they may not have been motivated immediately in an untutored brain. And in all this the system of penalties and rewards that individuals experienced had to connect neurologically and resonate with those penalties and rewards involved in the animal-ritual communications that previously sufficed to structure social behavior without verbal explanations because this was the route to the necessary, genetically based motivation system.

Also the penalties and rewards would have to match what statistically was experienced as meted out by the social system and by the larger ecosystem surrounding it. In addition to the long-term requirement that the implicit and explicit promises of delayed rewards be valid was the problem of keeping these promises and threats (sanctions) constantly alive in the central nervous systems of the population. Religions, as the core institutions for the transmission of these vital or sacred schemes or promised later rewards and punishments in a sociocultural organism, necessarily became involved in a constant round of sacred rituals in which animal-level ritual was combined with the new, coadapted myth-level rites to insure remembrance and observance of the viable culturetypic modifications in the expression of the genetically patterned mechanisms for perceiving and responding to signals of what is good or evil for life. From the perspective of contemporary history of religions this stage is called that of the formation of the symbolic myths.

The religious myths provided a special category of a culturetype that could connect the more complex, verbally programmed patterns in the brain with the nonverbal and the more central motivational core of the brain.[31] They functioned to shape the most fundamental or ultimate values that must be held in common in the brain structures of a population of anthropoids if they were to live in symbiosis with a beneficial cultural organism. These myths, like the related rituals before them, were the product not so much of conscious planning as of the same kind of wisdom-generating and wisdom-selecting forces that have operated eternally in the evolution of living systems: the natural selection of the more viable or stable among an assortment of boundary conditions guiding homeostatic energy-flow patterns at increasing levels of remove from thermodynamic equilibrium.[32] The selection of the pattern most fit to ensure the survival of the symbiotic populations of anthropoids and cultural organisms was accomplished by the greater flourishing of those symbiotic memes and genes that conjointly produced the more viable or persistent ecosystemic patterns just as in the previous evolution of the coadapted gene pools of two or more symbiotic species to form a more advantageous ecosystem. The only new thing is that the memory of the culturetype was never in the genes but only in the brains and the related artifacts generated by those brains and found in human cultural communities.

It follows from this hypothesis that all religions are products of the same general process of selection that produced animal and plant life. The religious gods of the life-explaining myths are themselves the naturally selected symbols which effectively motivated within the brain structures of those times the suitable response patterns to the realities that were in fact the creators and determiners of human destiny as now understood scientifically. Religious wisdom, like Walter B. Cannon's celebrated *Wisdom of the Body* (wisdom of the genes), is itself a product of the evolution of the reality system (nature).[33] The gods were indeed proper symbols of the hidden realities that explained why life was as it was and why men must do what the combined and fairly well-coadapted cultural and genetic information in them told them they must do. The same myths also were the sciences of their day. They told primitive peoples about the origins and major developments of themselves in relation to the world they live in. The sacred knowledge of what was basically good or evil was conjoined with and inseparable from their knowledge of the world and all things in it. Of course the basic good always was tied inherently to the maintenance of the implicit contracts of reciprocal altruism between an individual and his symbiont, the sociocultural organism, and thus to the ultimate requirements of the ecosystem (the gods, collectively God) for viability.

I shall not here discuss a later level in the evolutionary emergence of a rational, analytic stage of discourse in religion—theology—some two or three thousand years ago, or how that development in turn was tied to the earlier stages by analogous requirements in the nature of the hierarchies of such systems. But I shall conclude by calling attention to the fact that it also follows from this hypothesis concerning the origin of human civilization that religions or some functionally equivalent cultural agencies are essential for any civilization at any stage, including ours, since, beginning with their genetically based rituals and on through myths and theologies, they are the cultural source of coadapted basic values which motivate that genetically selfish ape-man to serve his symbiotic sociocultural organism. While this may appear to be serving his potential genetic competitors, since a civilized society includes many more than one's close kin, religion transforms genetic selfishness into reciprocal altruism between the ape-man and the sociocultural organism in which he abides by so structuring the behavior of the inhabiting ape-man as to enhance the inclusive fitness of all ape-men who are allowed to remain. It does this by guaranteeing a system of reciprocal altruisms and a higher probability for genetic success in competition with those ape-men who do not dwell in such a favorable ecological niche as that supplied by a well-adapted or viable sociocultural organism.

From the standpoint of individual ape-men the sociocultural organism is simply a more favorable ecological habitat, even though it is structured by their collaboration with the brains of the genetic competitors. According to this hypothesis the operations of nature will select against and diminish or eliminate any civilization, state, or lesser sociocultural organism if it fails to provide this kind of favorable habitat for the ape-men who inhabit it. And any ape-men whose genetic disposition or whose inadequate enculturation fails to produce behavior suitably devoted to the cultural code will be punished, driven out, or killed—thus inhibiting their individual inclusive fitness and ridding the sociocultural organism of a "cancer." The viable sociocultural organism thus has captured in its tradition—and sometimes in the conscious thought of some of its inhabiting ape-men—the wisdom that there can be enhanced inclusive fitness for individuals through certain kinds of cooperation with what otherwise would be competitors. I would note that ancient theologies captured and reflected this wisdom in their doctrines of man. Saint Paul's organic analogy of the Christian community and the many notions of loyalty to brotherhoods of the spirit transcending or enhancing genetic kin loyalties are examples.

But I shall make a special point of the central notion of the major religious doctrines or theologies that is far ahead of contemporary secular thinking and more in keeping with evolutionary theory for understanding man's place in the scheme of things. This is the notion of man's dependence upon the system of the objective requirements posed by a nature that is much more than human, to which all living systems must adapt, the ultimate reality system, whether we call it nature or God. Of course the thus-far evolved and surviving systems of genetic and cultural information obviously have adapted more or less their hedonic or motivational norms to this reality system. But clearly for a high civilization requiring altruism to genetic competitors this reality system, which is the ultimate criterion for all human values, does not allow us a genetically programmed hedonism that is unconditioned or unrefined, as Campbell's presidential address correctly indicated. When I say unconditioned hedonism I do not mean to deny the hedonic basis of motivation but to assert that some equivalent to the hitherto evolved religious modes of conditioning the genetically based hedonic response patterns is necessary if we are to continue the symbiosis that transforms the expression of 99-percent-anthropoid genes into organisms with sufficient altruism to nonkin conspecifics to make civilization possible.

NOTES

1. The interdisciplinary character of evolutionary theory has existed from its beginning when several areas of geological and biological sciences in the nineteenth century contributed to the formulation of the evolutionary picture. In the twentieth century, with significant new developments from the chemical, physical, and astrophysical sciences to illuminate the evolutionary picture from the more physical levels of analysis on the earlier side and significant new developments from the psychosocial and humanistic disciplines (especially early were contributions from the study of language) to illuminate human development and cultural evolution in more recent levels of emergence, the modern pictures of the phylogeny and ontogeny of man are truly interdisciplinary. An interesting testimony of this is given by the astronomer Eric J. Chaisson in his "The Scenario of Cosmic Evolution," first published in *Harvard Magazine* 80 (November-December 1977): 20–33 and with minor changes republished as "Cosmic Evolution: A Synthesis of Matter and Life" in *Zygon* 14 (March 1979): 23–39. Chaisson, after illustrating the range of disciplines involved in understanding human evolution, in his last paragraph provides an excellent summary in which he indicates that the "philosophy that we are the product of comsic evolution [is] very much an interdisciplinary approach, interweaving knowledge from virtually every approach, interweaving knowledge from virtually every subject a university can offer." For a different but relevant discussion of systems theory see H. Sodak and A. Iberall, "Homeokinetics: A Physical Science for Complex Systems," *Science* 201 (1978): 579-82.

2. Edward O. Wilson, *Sociobiology: The New Synthesis* (Cambridge, Mass.: Harvard University Press, 1975). In his glossary, on p. 595, he defines "sociobiology" this way. In chap. 1 he defines the term more fully. I use the terms "altruistic behavior" and "altruism" also to designate the kind of behavior which is defined in Wilson's glossary more operationally or objectively than in Webster's dictionary. Wilson's glossary defines altruism as "self-destructive behavior performed for the benefit of others." This avoids specifying just what is the self that is destroyed. As will become clear from this paper, I limit the self-destruction to the phenotype but exclude the genes, which some writers include (I think mistakenly) in their definition of what is risked in altruistic behavior. I would include more behavior than the above definition by Wilson, namely, all behavior that even risks some probability of self-destruction.

3. C. H. Waddington, *The Ethical Animal* (New York: Atheneum Publishers, 1961), esp. p. 131.

4. Herbert A. Simon, *The Sciences of the Artificial* (Cambridge, Mass.: M.I.T. Press, 1969), esp. p. 25: "A man, viewed as a behaving system, is quite simple. The apparent complexity of his behavior over time is largely a reflection of the complexity of the environment in which he finds himself."

5. S. L. Washburn, "Human Behavior and the Behavior of Other Animals," *American Psychologist* 33 (May 1978): 405-18.

6. Donald T. Campbell, "On the Conflicts between Biological and Social Evolution and between Psychology and Moral Tradition," *American*

Psychologist 30 (December 1975): 1103-26 (reprinted in *Zygon* 11[September 1976]: 167-208).

7. Ibid., p. 202.

8. Wilson (n. 2 above), p. 379.

9. Ibid., p. 362.

10. Ibid., pp. 354, 356-58.

11. George C. Williams, *Adaptation and Natural Selection* (Princeton, N.J.: Princeton University Press, 1966). This is perhaps the classic American statement of the problem, clearly arguing and documenting with evidence that the currently established model or view of how natural selection works does not allow for selection of groups within an ecological niche. See esp. p. 95 for the pithy statement of the main point: "The natural selection of alternative alleles can foster the production of individuals willing to sacrifice their lives for their offspring, but never for mere friends."

12. Wilson (n. 2 above) provides details on various aspects of the genetic problems and potentialities for producing altruism. See p. 120 for "reciprocal altruism."

13. Williams (n. 11 above), pp. 246-47, points out that for the symbiotic mutualisms, such as the termite and its intestinal symbionts, "the selection of alternative alleles can simply and adequately explain the origin and maintenance of such relationships."

14. Alfred E. Emerson, in "Ecology, Evolution and Society" (*American Naturalist* 77 [1943]: 117-18), his 1941 presidential address to the Ecological Scoiety of America, gave some pioneering analyses of interspecific cooperative communities, where he found populations from several species operating as an ecosystem so closely adapted and effectively coordinated as to warrant being called a supraorganism. In numerous earlier and later papers (e.g., n. 20 below) he provided a wealth of detailed evidence on the coadaptation of the genes and correlated phenotypic structures and behaviors of several species to constitute such an integrated interspecific living system. My many discussions with him were a prime source of my hypothesis of the sociocultural organism as a truly independently selected species to account for human altruism, after Campbell had led me to take Williams's taboo on group selection seriously. The recent discovery that human beings are themselves symbiotic systems is described in a fascinating, poetic form by Lewis Thomas in his *The Lives of a Cell* (New York: Viking Press, 1974) in the chapter "Organelles as Organisms." An earlier and more detailed summary of the explanation of such phenomena is given by Lynn Margulis, "Symbiosis and Evolution," *Scientific American* 225 (August 1971): 48-57.

15. Richard Dawkins, *The Selfish Gene* (Oxford: Oxford University Press, 1976). This is a lively and readable introduction for nonspecialists into the basic problem of the selfish gene and the big paradox of human altruism for sociobiology. For the term "idene," the cultural analogue of the genotype's gene, we are indebted to Henry Alexander Murray's quip in a 1959 conference of the American Academy of Arts and Sciences on "The Concept of Progress in Terms of Biological and Cultural Evolution." Hudson Hoagland and Julian Huxley used "idea" deriving from Murray's use. For Huxley's statement see *Nature* 196 (1962): 203. Dawkins introduces "meme" in his last chapter.

16. F. S. C. Northrop's "The Methods and Grounds of Religious Knowledge" was published as chap. 23 in his *The Logic of the Sciences and the Humanites* (New York: Macmillan Co., 1947) and was reprinted in *Zygon* 12 (December 1977): 237-88. The term "way of talking" I owe to Philipp Frank who commonly used this phrase when he sought to calm the antipathies of persons from different disciplines and ideologies when they were affronted by the seeming incredibility of terms used in the alien jargon. Frank's "ways of talking" may be a more simple and useful term than the "paradigms" of Thomas Kuhn, for whom he was a mentor, incidentally. For an insight into how a physicist's way of talking in no way diminishes the importance of subjective knowing or "speaking in the first person" see P. W. Bridgman, *The Way Things Are* (Cambridge, Mass.: Harvard University Press, 1959), esp. the preface and introduction.

17. Most of my papers since the early 1950s have been concerned with the role of religion in human cultural evolution and hence with religion's real function in biological and cosmic evolution; I was early educated to understand each successive stage of evolution as riding piggyback on all those prior to it. Most of what I have written have been referred to in three recent papers in *Zygon*: "The Human Prospect and the 'Lord of History,'" *Zygon* 10 (September 1975): 299-375; "The Source of Civilization in the Natural Selection of Coadapted Information in Genes and Culture," ibid. 11 (September 1976): 263-303; and "What Does Determine Human Destiny?—Science Applied to Interpret Religion," ibid. 12 (December 1977): 336-89.

18. See n. 11 above.

19. Dawkins (n. 15 above), esp. the last few pages.

20. Alfred E. Emerson's "Dynamic Homeostasis: A Unifying Principle in Organic, Social, and Ethical Evolution," (*Zygon* 3[June 1968]: 129-68) contains on p. 141 his reference to his analysis of the concept of "supraorganism" published in 1952. He developed the notion in many papers describing the essential cooperation of members of several species whose interactions were difficult to distinguish from that of an organism and none of which could continue to exist without the contributions of the others. A recent summary of his position appeared in his "Tertiary Fossil Species of Rhinotermitidae . . . ," *Bulletin of the American Museum of Natural History* 146 (1971): 245-303.

21. Williams (n. 11 above) concurs in principle that natural selection of alternative alleles can account for symbiotic cooperation among species, even though it forbids selection of cooperative altruism within a species except for close family kin. But he does not seem to be so impressed as Emerson with the degree of complex organization possible through such coadaptation.

22. The term "value core" of the culturetype is used here to indicate that certain information in culturetypes as well as in genotypes now is understood clearly to be more critical than other information where variability is more tolerable. In culturetypes the value core is designated properly as the more vital or sacred information, the alteration of which would lead to the breakdown of the sociocultural system; other patterns of the culture can tolerate much more variation. In general the religious information in a culture has this character of sacrality. Whether a cultural brother is a tinker,

tailor, cowboy, or sailor is not critical for arousing attitudes of liking or disliking him; but whether he properly manifests the same morals and ideology may make for deep affection or extinction.

23. Concerning the genetic coadaptation in ape-men for symbiosis with the central or religious values of culturetypes, Hudson Hoagland long ago suggested that "the brain is first and foremost an organ of survival . . . by natural selection. . . . [Man's] unique psychosocial evolution has had a feedback on his biological evolution further to develop his brain. . . . The ability to form meaningful configurations that encompass large segments of the environment is a property of the more highly developed brains, and a good case can be made for the view that man's concerns with science, philosophy, political ideologies, and theologies are a reflection of a basic property of his nervous system to integrate extensive configurations relating himself to his environment." The above words come from Hoagland's "The Brain and Crises in Human Values" (*Zygon* 1 [June 1966]: 140-57) given at the Institute on Religion in an Age of Science summer conference on Star Island in 1964. See esp. pp. 153-55: "Some Religious Implications of Biological Knowledge." A more recent IRAS paper adds to a long succession of papers on the role of genetically programmed characteristics of the brain in religion: Eugene G. d'Aquili's "The Neurobiological Bases of Myth and Concepts of Deity," *Zygon* 13 (December 1978): 257-75.

24. Emerson (nn. 14 and 20 above) elaborated in many papers the exquisite detail of synthetic operations between two or more species in shaping the viable or adaptive behavior of symbiotic supraorganisms.

25. I think the papers published in *Zygon* and the work of hundreds associated with the formation and activities of IRAS and the Center for Advanced Study in Religion and Science (CASIRAS) demonstrate this possibility.

26. Wilson (n. 2 above), p. 120.

27. Noam Chomsky pioneered in showing the coadaptation between human languages and genetically structured brain patterns.

28. Paul D. MacLean's "The Brain's Generation Gap: Some Human Implications" (*Zygon* 8 [June 1973]: 113-17) gives a good picture of the hierarchical and phylogenetic structures of the brain. The role of animal-level ritual, which MacLean finds programmed in the lower or reptilian brain, was brought first to my attention on reading Konrad Lorenz's *On Aggression* (New York: Harcourt, Brace & World, 1966).

29. Lawrence Kohlberg's "Indoctrination versus Relativity in Value Education (*Zygon* 4 [December 1971]: 285-310) is illustrative of his development of the stages in human moral development. The close relation of man and chimpanzee has been demonstrated in a new way by studies in the evolution of macromolecules in the past couple of decades. See, for instance, Mary-Claire King and A. C. Wilson, "Evolution at Two Levels in Humans and Chimpanzees," *Science* 188 (April 11, 1975): 107.

30. It is well known that the environment and the genotype in their interaction constrain the brain to present a more or less successful adaptive response to what under the circumstances is required for life. See Hoagland, for instance, in n. 23 above. Whenever the brain completely fails so to

perform, nature's selection weeds it out and leaves on the scene only those brains that have been successful. Psychotherapists are also familiar with the fact that the same forces prohibit a brain that for any length of time produces a self-awareness that denies the worth or hope for the future of the self. But in the evolutionary emergence of increasingly complex cultural transmissions of information to the brains of ape-men the genetically programmed brain cannot be prepared to handle all the complex adjustments necessary to function in this way without help from the culture. The geneticist Theodosius Dobzhansky sensed this and expressed it in our conversations on many occasions and wrote of it in his "An Essay on Religion, Death, and Evolutionary Adaptation," *Zygon* 1 (December 1966): 317-31, the publication of a paper given at the same 1964 IRAS conference referred to in n. 23 above. Dobzhansky, along with others, inferred from archaeological findings of human burials around 100,000 B.C. that religions already had begun to be a necessary and significant cultural institution for informing brains how to transcend what otherwise would seem to be man's fragmentariness, to provide some plausible source of meaning and hope as the consciously expanding horizons of man had to adapt to information that the genotype had never "been aware of."

31. IRAS conferences and *Zygon* papers have provided numerous papers by persons in different disciplines all reflecting the function of religious myths to alleviate emotionally destructive fears, none perhaps more graphically and authoritatively than Erwin Goodenough's "An Historian of Religion Tries to Define Religion," *Zygon* 2 (March 1967): 7-22, another paper given at the above-mentioned 1964 IRAS Star Island conference. Following Goodenough one can say that religious myths are the stage "scenery" or the culturally artifacted loci that define the stage setting on which we act out our lives. It is a different scene from what the untutored or unenculturated animal sees, for no genes can be selected to be adaptive for circumstances to which only culturetypes are being selected fo on page 113).

32. I revert here to my scientific setting for life portrayed physically as a dissipative flow pattern. It comes out of the work particularly of I. Prigogine but was introduced to me by Aharon Katchalsky-Katzir, whose "Thermodynamics of Flow and Biological Organization" was published in *Zygon* 6 (June 1971): 99-125. It is a paper closely related to J. Bronowski's "New Concepts in the Evolution of Complexity: Stratified Stability and Unbounded Plans," *Zygon* 5 (March 1969): 18-35. It is fascinating to contemplate that these living patterns in the dissipative flow streams of the cosmos have been made more stable than the biblical mountains which were symbols of eternity. This stability we now know is produced by the stable, continually replicated and selected memory patterns that provide homeostasis, or, as Emerson suggested, "dynamic homeostasis." Some of these patterns as produced by DNA are hundreds of millions of years old, going back to times when the continents of the earth and their mountain systems were utterly different from today.

33. Walter B. Cannon, *The Wisdom of the Body* (New York: W. W. Norton & Co., 1932).

INDEX

Abbot, Francis Ellingwood, 75
Adaptation, 18, 77, 126, 192, 196.
  See also Coadaptation;
  Evolution
Altruism, 201-33
  and genes, 162,172, 206-09
  animal, 167
  human, 11, 17, 18, 22, 42, 121,
    162, 176-77, 204-10,
    214-17, 222, 227
American Academy of Arts and
  Sciences, 15, 16
American Psychological
  Association, 18, 151
American Psychologist, 151
Andover Newton Theological
  School, 14
Ape-man (hominid), 20-21, 55,
  201-28
Aquinas, Saint Thomas, 59
Aristotle, 117
Ashby, Ross, 132
Augustine, Saint, 104

Barth, Karl, 10
Behavior, 27, 44, 47, 83, 139, 173
  good, 63-66
Belief, religious, 13, 34
  in God, necessity of, 117-18
  major elements of, 116
  truth in, according to science, 13,
    119
Biology, molecular, 19
  evolutionary, 10
  theoretical, 11
Boorman, S. A., 222
Booth, Edwin Prince, 15
Boyd, Robert, 164, 182
Brain, 20, 22, 28, 36, 42, 54-55,
  59-60, 64-65, 83, 91-95,
  157-58, 173, 183, 192.
  See also Central nervous system
  structure of, 159-61, 164

Bronowski, J., 108, 132, 152, 170,
  195-96
Browning, Don, 9, 11
Buddha, 23, 121
Burhoe, Ralph Wendell, 9-11
  and Hoagland, Hudson, eds.,
    *Evolution and Man's
    Progress,* 17

Campbell, Donald T., 18, 23,
  151-53, 156, 161-65, 174,
  178, 203-4, 208, 214, 217,
  220-22, 228
Cannon, Walter B., 53, 226
Center for Advanced Study in
  Religion and Science, 9, 16
Centre for Advanced Study in
  Theology and the Sciences, 16,
  25n. *See also* Centre for
  Advanced Study in Religion
  and Science
Central nervous system, 28, 33, 36,
  54-55, 64-65, 145. *See also*
  Brain
Chaisson, Eric J., 201, 229n
Chicago Cluster Theological
  Schools, 16
Christian faith, 10
Cloak, F. T., 164
Club of Rome, 113, 146
Coadaptation, 21 22, 155, 166-69,
  173-75, 178-86, 192, 214-16,
  221
Coming Great Church Conference,
  15
Communication, 142, 189-91, 223.
  See also Language
Communism, 114, 117
Comte, Auguste, 178
Confucius, 23
Competition, genetic, 162-64, 166,
  174

235

Theology *(Continued)*
  Religion; Science; Truth
  defined as a religious science, 37,
    114-115; as answers to
    questions of religious
    concern, 47
  normative, 11
Thermodynamics, second law of,
  51-52, 122-23, 131-32
Thomas, Lewis, 19, 20
  Lives of a Cell, 19, 20
Tillich, Paul, 218
Toynbee, [Arnold], 116
Trivers, Robert L., 165
Truth, 22, 39-41, 193-96. *See also*
  Belief; Epistemology;
  Knowledge, valid; Reality
  system; Scientific theory
  and religion, 115-16
  and science, 115

Uliassi, Edward C., 164
Ultimate concerns, indicative of
  religion, theology, 115
Understanding. *See* Belief;
  Epistemology; Knowledge;
  Religion, understanding of;
  Theology; Truth
University of Chicago Press, 16

Values, 20, 29, 30-35, 36-42, 46,
  49-53, 63, 217. *See also* Good
  and evil; Religion
  and facts, 36
  and genes, 54, 64
  and information, 63
  and science, 38
  cultural, 11
  hierarchy of, 31-33, 34-35, 55,
    62-64, 67
  intrinsic, 50-53

Waddington, C. H., 202
Wald, George, 15, 62, 69n, 145,
  196
Wallace, Anthony F. C., 34, 53, 64,
  118, 186
Washburn, S. L., 202-3
Wiener, Norbert, 51-52, 63, 131
Williams, George C., 17, 28,
  161-65, 168-69, 178-79,
  207-8, 231n
  *Adaptation and Natural
    Selection,* 18, 162-63, 214,
    230n
Wilson, E. O., 17, 158, 165, 174,
  184, 202, 204-5, 215-17, 222
  Sociobiology, 163-64, 175, 208,
    229n

Zygon, 9, 10, 16, 36, 174